HONEYBUBBLE & CO.

OTHER BOOKS IN
THE FOUNTAIN LIBRARY

THE FOUNTAIN LIBRARY

HONEYBUBBLE & CO.

BY

A. P. HERBERT, M.P.

METHUEN & CO. LTD. LONDON

First Published . . . *November 8th 1928*
Second and Cheaper Edition . *November 1931*
Third Edition (Fountain Library) 1936

TO
GWEN HERBERT

I have to thank the Proprietors of *Punch* for their courtesy in permitting me to collect from their columns these profound studies of life and character, literature, drama, and the film.

A. P. H.

CONTENTS

CONTENTS

MR. HONEYBUBBLE

I

COSTS ME A HAT

I FIRST met Mr. Honeybubble in a liner crossing the Atlantic. Generally the Ship's Bore does not impress himself upon you till about the second day out, but the *Cecic* had scarcely sidled away from the landing-stage before I heard his unmistakable tones. He stood beside me at the rail with a young woman, to whom, in a high-pitched, harsh but kindly voice, like a well-intentioned saw, he pointed out the various objects of interest on the Liverpool shore. Evidently he was an old traveller, for he had already hidden away his bowler and wore the dingy cloth cap in blue and white checks which is considered suitable for heavy weather on the promenade deck. He had mild and watery blue eyes and a melancholy little moustache in pale grey.

' That's the Liver building, my dear,' he was saying. ' The birds on the roof are livers, and they say that's how Liverpool got its name, though of course they don't call it Līverpool, but Lǐverpool—well, it doesn't sound right, somehow, the other way. Some people say there never was such a bird, but I don't know about that. Anyhow, I never heard of any one who'd seen a liver, to my recollection. And that's the Cunard building—the Cunard steamers, you know. We shan't see the cathedral to-day, I dare say, because of the mist, but it's up on the hill there ; you'd see it well if it wasn't for the mist. Take care, my dear, you'll drop your bag in the water.'

The young lady seemed to pay very little attention to these remarks, and soon I felt rather than saw that the gentleman was proposing to address himself to me. Possessed by that distrust and loathing of my fellow-passengers with which every good Englishman begins a journey I declined to look his way, more especially as I suspected him of belonging to that most deadly species, the Bore Benevolent, to whom it is impossible to be rude, from whom there is no escape. With six days in a ship ahead of him a man cannot be too careful about his acquaintances.

And presently my worst fears were confirmed.

I felt a gentle pressure on my arm, and the Voice said, ' Excuse me, sir, but if you're not careful you'll lose your hat.'

The Voice was so full of good intention that I could not ignore it.

' Oh, thanks,' I said meekly, and jammed my hat more firmly on my head.

' You'll find there's a lot more wind before very long, out in the river. And it catches a hat before a man knows where he is.'

' Oh, thanks. I shan't be here very long,' I said with conviction.

' You'll excuse my speaking, won't you ? I've seen so many hats lost that way.'

' Very kind of you,' I murmured helplessly, feeling the toils grow tighter.

' I generally wear a cap myself. You haven't brought a cap, perhaps ? '

' No.'

' Pity. It looks funny arriving in a foreign country with no hat. A man feels a fool.'

I had no intention of arriving in a foreign country with no hat, but did not think it worth while to say so. I wanted to go away, but my fatal good nature detained me.

' Yes' I said.

' I remember a very dear friend of mine,' went on the nameless monster whom I now know to be Mr. Honeybubble ; ' he lost his hat in Southampton Water. Just such another hat as yours.'

' Really ? ' I said.

' Yes. A grey felt hat. Oh, dear, we did laugh ! And only the minute before I'd warned him too. " Put your cap on," I said, " Mr. Rugg, or use a hat-guard." And that reminds me. Pansy,' he said, turning back to the young lady—' did you pack the hat-guard, my dear ? '

' I think so, father—in the green bag.'

' First time I've crossed without it if you didn't, my dear. But I'm forgetting myself. This is my daughter, sir. And while I'm about it I'd better introduce myself. My name's Honeybubble. Ben Honeybubble. Pansy, my dear, this is—Mr.—— But I don't think I got your name, sir ? '

In all my experience of steamships this was the quickest thing yet. Here we were, not a mile from Water Street, and already I was practically a member of the man's family. And the whole Atlantic before us !

I played with the notion of giving a false name and address ; but such is the sweetness of my character and such was the disarming geniality of Mr. Honeybubble that I had not the heart.

'Haddock,' I said. And 'Penrose Haddock,' I added, for I felt that it would not be long before we got to Christian names.

'Haddock. Ah!' said Mr. Honeybubble with a contented sigh. 'Miss Honeybubble—Mr. Haddock. And now we're all correct. I was just telling Mr. Haddock, my dear, that he ought to be careful of his hat. He put me in mind of Tom Rugg, who lost his hat in Southampton Water. I've told you that story, I dare say?'

'Yes, father,' said Pansy, a shade hurriedly, I thought.

'Which reminds me. I wonder if you'd be so kind as to run down and see if that hat-guard's in the bag. I dare say Mr. Haddock would like the loan of it.'

'Certainly, father,' said Pansy, tearing herself away from her wistful contemplation of the shore.

'Oh, *please* no!' I cried.

'Oh, but of course!' said Pansy.

'You really mustn't——'

'Oh, but I'd like to——'

'She doesn't mind,' said Honeybubble, patting her cheek. 'She's a good girl—aren't you, Pansy?'

'But perhaps Mr. Haddock doesn't *want* it, father?'

At this horrid thought a little cloud so sad passed over Honeybubble's brow that I hastened to reassure him.

'I'd love it,' I said, though indeed I had hideous recollections of a long black elastic contrivance with nickel clips at either end by which, in my extreme youth, the straw hat was tethered to the Eton jacket. 'It's awfully kind of you. But as a matter of fact I shan't be on deck much longer. I'm—er—I'm going below.'

'Not squeamish, I hope?' said Honeybubble.

'No, no,' I said hastily, for fear that Pansy should be despatched for a sea-sick remedy. 'I'm going to write some letters.'

'Oh, well, you may need it to-morrow. There—run along, my dear.'

'Very well, father'; and the dutiful child departed.

'A good girl, Pansy,' said Honeybubble. 'And a great one for reading. You wouldn't believe what that girl reads. SCOTT and DOOMAS partic'ly. You're going over to America, I take it, Mr. Haddock?'

Since the ship, so far as I knew, was not to call at any other continent I could not well deny this.

'Oh, well,' said he, 'perhaps we'll see something of you. It's wonderful, I always say, what friendships one makes on board ship.'

'Wonderful,' I murmured absently. I was considering how I could tactfully escape; for so great already was my respect for Honeybubble's powers that I knew that once Pansy returned with the hat-guard, nothing could prevent him from fitting the thing to my hat. And I should then suffer for six days the indescribable humiliation of an anchored hat. I saw myself the mock of all the female passengers—the absurd young man who had his hat tied on. I saw my hat, my new gent's Stetson, blowing off in mid-Atlantic and dangling round my legs at the end of its string, or soaring skywards like a toy balloon. It was too much.

'There's generally somebody,' Mr. Honeybubble was saying, 'I take a fancy to. And I somehow cottoned to you at once.'

'I'm awfully glad,' I murmured feebly and wildly looked about me. One cannot simply leave a man while he is in the middle of that kind of remark.

'Yes,' he continued; 'and I was just wondering if we couldn't meal together, perhaps.'

'I don't think——' I began.

'Here you are, father,' said a breathless voice behind us. And there was Pansy, and in her hand the hat-guard. It was just what I expected, only the clips were gun-metal instead of nickel.

'Thank you, my dear. Now let me fit it on for you, Mr. Haddock,' said Mr. Honeybubble. 'I know the way of it.'

Helpless, I raised my hand to remove the hat.

And the extraordinary thing was that at that moment *my hat did blow off*.

My hat, my new Stetson, swooped down to the Mersey and merrily bobbed astern at a good ten knots. We gazed at it in silence.

'Well, there now!' said Mr. Honeybubble at last, half in triumph and half in tears.

'Well, did you ever?' said Pansy.

'But I thought you had *hold* of it,' said Honeybubble. ''Pon my word, it almost looked as if you did it on purpose. Ha!'

'Ha, ha!' I replied. 'What an idea, Mr. Honeybubble!'

II

COTTONS TO ME

I NEVER knew a bore so benevolent as Mr. Honeybubble. He oozes goodness, loving-kindness and *ennui*. He longs to succour or to benefit his fellows, particularly that unfortunate to whom he has for the moment attached himself. Though he may be driving his victim mad, he does it with the best intentions. Never in my acquaintance with the man have I been blind to this noble side of his character. But ' side ' ? Do I say ' side ' ? The whole man is good. And even when he has bored me most I have always at the same time guiltily rebuked myself for not loving him. Indeed the more frightfully he is boring me the more heartily do I remind myself of his fundamental benignity and good nature, which, after all, in the long account, we know, are qualities more valuable than mere charm, and so forth.

After my hat had been blown into the Mersey from the deck of the R.M.S. *Cecic*, Mr. Honeybubble's remorse and sympathy knew no bounds. So concerned was he lest I should catch cold uncovered on deck that I was base enough to take him seriously and seized the opportunity to escape below. I felt guilty about doing this ; but I did it.

Once below I went straight to the saloon, sought out the Chief Steward and made sure that Mr. Honeybubble and I were not at the same table. I blamed myself while I did this ; the stings of conscience and humanity pricked me severely, I can assure you ; however, I did it.

I then went up to the smoking-room with a book. I went to the smoking-room because I had an instinct that Honeybubble did not smoke, though I was less sure of the daughter. Out on deck the sun shone. The last view of Liverpool receding up the Mersey was fine and striking. I should have liked very much to go out and look at the water and the ships. But Honeybubble and Pansy were on deck. So I went to the smoking-room.

For this action, for these thoughts, I reproached myself bitterly at the time. As I do now.

My instinct, as instinct usually is, was hopelessly at fault.

Almost immediately I heard the now familiar tones, resonant, though grating, and in came Honeybubble filling a pipe. He stopped to hold open the door for a very old gentleman and proceeded to help him off with his coat, talking kindly the while. By the time he had finished I could see that the object of his attentions was in a condition of speechless fury ; and I felt sorry for Honeybubble.

I watched him covertly.

His eyes roamed the room anxiously, and when they fell upon me, to my intense dismay I saw his face light up like a cornfield on a distant hill in fitful April when the sun falls suddenly upon it from behind a cloud and the heart of the husbandman is gladdened. I had not till then thought much of his remark that he had ' cottoned to me ' ; it now took on a most serious significance.

He came straight across to me, beaming under his woolly moustache.

' *Having a bit of a read ?* ' he cried. ' That's right.' And he settled himself comfortably in the next chair.

' Yes,' I said, and, as one engrossed, I glued my eyes to my book, which I discovered to be upside down.

' You're not a smoker, Mr. Haddock ? ' he said, lighting his pipe.

' Yes, I am,' I said.

' Don't fancy it just now, perhaps ? '

' Oh, well,' I said, ' I think I will——'

In fact I had been deliberately denying myself a

smoke ; but somehow, now that Honeybubble was with me, I felt that I must smoke or die. I pulled out my pipe and pouch.

' 'Baccy ? ' said Honeybubble kindly.

' Thanks ; I have some.'

' Try some of mine, won't you ? '

' Oh, thanks. I have my own here.'

I hastily rammed a great wad of tobacco into my pipe. Other men's tobaccos are invariably vile.

But not so easily are the Honeybubbles of this world prevented from doing good.

' Now do. I insist ! ' he said, holding out his wretched pouch. ' You'll find it a nice cool smoke. It's the Sweet Pea mixture, I've smoked it for twenty-five years.'

' No, really,' I protested, ' I'm filled already.'

' Oh, well, that's easy remedied,' said my benefactor. ' Allow me ' ; and, seizing my pouch and pipe from my nerveless fingers, he carefully with a pen-knife extracted from my pipe my own tobacco, returned it to my pouch and held out his own again with so radiant a beam upon his countenance that, as usual, I had not the heart to be annoyed. One had the impression that by making me smoke his detestable Sweet Pea he was spreading happiness throughout the ship.

I slowly filled my pipe with Sweet Pea, which was black and coarse and full of objects like pistachio-nuts.

Nor was I compelled to light my pipe unaided. Honeybubble produced a patent petrol-lighter (interestingly constructed out of a German shell), and after that what is called, I believe, a ' Smoker's Companion,' an ingenious metal contrivance with a tool for the ramming of tobacco into a pipe and another for the poking of it when it will not draw. Honeybubble made me employ all these weapons till I was spent with saying ' Thank you ' and nearly mad with the suppression of other sentiments.

When he had got my pipe going for me at last I returned to my book and read fourteen words.

' YOU'RE FOND OF READING, I EXPECT, MR. HADDOCK ? ' shouted Honeybubble then.

' Yes,' I said—not rudely, you understand, but still not raising my eyes.

' My daughter Pansy's a great one for reading,' the steam-roller continued undaunted, ' SCOTT and DOOMAS, partic'ly. A very fine writer, SCOTT—so she tells me.'

I had that curious vivid sensation that what was happening had somewhere or other happened to me before.

This time, for an exception, I was able to identify the experience. It had happened about twenty minutes earlier, on the promenade-deck.

' Oh,' I said vaguely.

' Did you ever read *The Talisman*, now, Mr. Haddock ? '

' No,' I said incautiously.

' I've brought *The Talisman* with me this trip. Pansy told me I ought to read it and I said I'd try. Fine tale. But I don't seem to get very far with it. You've not read it, you say ? '

' No,' I said again, kicking myself ; for I foresaw that in about ten minutes I should be reading *The Talisman*.

' Well, I must lend it to you,' said Honeybubble. ' I'll slip down to the cabin in a minute and get it.'

My spirit was by now so nearly pulp that I did not even protest.

'It's funny how your face struck me the moment I saw you,' he continued. '"There's a man after your own heart, Honeybubble," I said; and it's very seldom I make a mistake with faces. How d'you like the smoke?'

'Charming—charming!' I murmured eagerly, anxious that the dear creature should not discover his mistake—at least not yet.

At that moment one of the pistachio-nuts in my pipe caught fire and burned with a great crackling—emitting foul fumes. I smoked on heroically, not moving a muscle.

'Good,' said Honeybubble. 'It's a pity we can't meal together,' he mused.

I looked about the crowded room. Just Heaven, what had I done that of all the teeming passengers in the ship this well-intentioned monster should have 'cottoned to' *me*? I saw about me a dozen elderly gentlemen, each of whom, I felt, would gladly fraternize with Honeybubble. But *mine—mine* was the face that struck him. Oh, Destiny!

'Pity we can't meal together,' he said again. 'Your table's fixed, I suppose?'

'Yes,' I said thankfully—but of course reproached myself as usual.

'Pity,' he replied. 'I'm at the Captain's table, I fancy. I generally get a seat there. It's difficult, but a word to the Purser does wonders.'

I could imagine that 'word.'

'Very nice,' I said, more thankful than ever.

'I wonder, now——' he mused. 'Well, I'll just slip down and get that book for you.'

Left to myself, I knocked out the awful Sweet Pea and wondered what base weakness in me it was that prevented me from telling Mr. Honeybubble how in just an hour his society had put me in a frenzy, and that, if I saw much more of him, I should certainly scream like a woman. Other men, I reflected, less worthy men too, would have known how to deal with him. But I——

'Well, there's *The Talisman*,' said the Voice behind me. 'And I've got a piece of news for you.'

Mr. Honeybubble's face was radiant with happiness. His eyes glistened with emotion.

'Great news,' he continued, shining all over. 'I've seen the Steward and he's promised to put you at the Captain's table—next to me. *Isn't that great?*'

'My dear fellow!' I cried, and I wrung him by the hand. I could say no more, my heart was too full.

III

WALKS THE ATLANTIC

On the second day out from Liverpool I lay about noon in a deck-chair in that blissful lethargy which is the whole art and object of travel in an Ocean Greyhound. The last meal still a pleasant recollection, the next meal already near enough to be contemplated with decency, the sun shining, the ship's motion steady and comfortable, the air fresh but not offensive. Moreover, it is at this hour that the most lovely of the lady passengers are generally to be seen pacing the deck, their faces prettily flushed, their hair and dress artistically disordered by the Atlantic breeze.

Moreover, at this hour their mothers, as a rule, have not yet left their cabins.

But however attractive the moving spectacle before me I kept a wary eye for Mr. Honeybubble. He had discovered that five-and-a-half times round the deck amounted to a mile, and he had early revealed himself as one of those agreeable lunatics who must walk exactly so many miles each day they are in a ship, and take more exercise in a week at sea than they do on land in a whole year. Many of these people are so assiduous that they may be said to walk across the Atlantic. Honeybubble was busily tramping round the deck at the moment, to the infinite annoyance of any ailing passengers in their bunks below. He had some wretched schoolboy in tow who had probably not walked so far before in his young life, but thought it unsporting to give up. Round the corner he came, head up, shoulders back, lurching to the roll of the ship, but nobly pretending that he was walking straight, breathing in the Atlantic through the nose and loudly expelling it through the mouth, and all the time talking, oozing geniality and diffusing about him the vapour of tedium.

I closed my eyes and lay as one in a deep sleep. I hated myself for the unkind thought that prompted this action ; but I had given up hope of evading Mr. Honeybubble by fair means. In twenty-four hours we had become bosom friends. He had loaded me with kindnesses. He had lent me a hat-guard and an old hat to replace the one so unfortunately lost in the Mersey. He had given me tobacco, forced huge cigars upon me. He had begged so earnestly to lend me that book *The Talisman* which lay now beside

me on the deck, that I was actually reading the work
to avoid further argument. He had secured me a
seat at the Captain's table (next to himself), and there,
so perfect his courtesy and thoughtfulness, I could
not for a moment be without the salt or suffer an
instant's anxiety about the mustard. Wherever I
went in the great ship—the smoking-room, the library,
the boat-deck—sooner or later Mr. Honeybubble would
be at my side to comfort and sustain me with kindly
thought and soothing conversation ; and if I fell into
the bilge I had no doubt that he would soon be there
also.

And yet, when I saw him lurching down the deck,
I closed my eyes and pretended to be asleep. Can
human baseness go further ?

' TWENTY-ONE,' he bellowed to the boy as he passed.
' ONE MORE FOR THE FOUR MILES. MY FRIEND MR.
HADDOCK'S TAKING A NAP, I SEE. PITY. HE MIGHT
HAVE JOINED US.'

When I opened my eyes again I was sorry to see
that that delicious little dark girl had also passed in
the interval. It was a pity she would walk so close
behind Honeybubble. And she was walking, unaccountably, alone—unaccountably because she was delicious
and because I had observed the previous evening that
she had a dragon for a mother. Perhaps her mother
was ill. I wished her mother no harm, but I hope
she was quite definitely ill.

I reflected sadly that, apart from Mr. Honeybubble,
I had so far made no friends on board. This might
be cause and effect. I had noticed that, however
crowded the smoking-room, by the time he had been
talking to me for twenty minutes we were the centre

of a large unpopulated open space. He seemed to have a capacity for creating a desert about him. I felt sometimes that he could have emptied Piccadilly Circus on a Saturday evening. And it might be that I was already known and avoided as Mr. Honeybubble's friend. This seemed hard.

But just then he sailed round the corner again, running free before the wind and holding on his check cap. I closed the eyes smartly.

Presently a body fell heavily into the chair beside me and a voice said loudly: ' *Taking forty winks, eh?* That's right.'

I half-opened the eyes, closed them again, and answered very drowsily : ' Yes.' There were still three-quarters of an hour to lunch, and it looked as if Honeybubble had done with walking. But surely he would respect a man's sleep !

It seemed not.

' Four miles we've done,' he shouted breezily. ' Twenty-two times round. Not bad before lunch, eh, Mr. Haddock ? '

' It's not very much,' I murmured, grudgingly. ' There's an old fellow there who's done more than that already.'

' I don't believe it, Mr. Haddock,' said Honeybubble in a Show-me-the-man tone.

I pointed to an elderly gentleman who for some time had been doing a conscientious totter round the deck, nose in air, like a long-distance runner about to collapse at the post.

' That old boy,' I lied, ' never lunches on less than five miles.'

' Don't he indeed ? ' said Honeybubble indomitably,

jumping to his feet. ' Well, Tommy, shall we knock off another couple, and show him ? You're not beaten, eh ? '

' Rather not,' said the miserable boy, dragging himself up from his chair.

As for Honeybubble, the real spirit of the man was coming out.

' I've always held the record,' he said, ' if you know what I mean, every boat I've been in so far. And I'm not going to give up yet. Come on, Tommy, my lad. Now why don't you take a turn, Mr. Haddock ? '

But my eyes were fast closed.

' Just a constitutional—eh ? Give you an appetite.'

But I was breathing peacefully through the nose. Not even Honeybubble should make me walk the deck.

' Well, that's a funny thing,' he said, ' Mr. Haddock's dropped off again, Tommy ; fancy that now. Pity. Well, off we go, then ! '

And off they went.

When I opened my eyes again (ashamed of myself, I need not say) the delicious little dark thing was just tripping past, lurching like the rest, but dainty and quick, her face more rosy and bewitching than before. She walked with purpose, as if she too had caught the fever and was just embarking on the fifteenth mile.

It occurred to me for the first time that perhaps after all I did need a little exercise. Just a constitutional.

I rose and zigzagged down the starboard side. I walked with purpose, as one attacking some Atlantic walking record, but not so fast as to overtake the young lady and not so slow as to be overtaken by

Honeybubble, who should be by now about half-way down the port side.

And so we walked and walked and walked. It would be a strange thing, I thought, if by the fourth or fifth mile the dark young thing did not drop her handkerchief, or lose that pleasant little hat in the breeze, or fall down in a faint, or somehow bring about an introduction. For this is how friendships, nay, and relations more important, are founded on the ocean. One party loses its heart, the other party loses its hat, and there you are. And why not? After all, it was my hat that, in a way, had thrown Honeybubble and myself together.

It is odd, I thought, that one cannot simply go up to a person and say: ' I like you. Let us walk together.' On board a steamship one very nearly can, but not quite—unless one is a Honeybubble.

But nothing seemed to happen to the dark young thing. She dropped nothing, not so much as a look over the shoulder. On, on she walked, five, six, seven times round that interminable deck. And then I lost count. Drooping, I followed, round and round, mile after mile, staggering like a drunken man and looking, I knew, not less ridiculous than Honeybubble. The Atlantic rolled and roared about us, but none of us took the smallest notice of it. We kept on walking.

When we had walked, as I judged, something like ten miles across the Atlantic, and I was about done for, a shudder ran through me. Behind me, close behind me, I had heard the unmistakable tones of Honeybubble, piercing without effort the tumult of ocean. Honeybubble, with his superior stamina, had caught us up— lapped us, as the athletes say. And now my march had been for nothing, for once Honeybubble came up with me I knew there could be no introduction. Probably the young lady would jump into the sea.

Up he came, hand over fist, tireless and breezy, and thumped me on the back.

' Blowing away the cobwebs, eh, Mr. Haddock ? ' he yelled. ' That's fine. You're looking more of a man already. You're looking more the thing. You're——'

But just at that moment, as luck would have it, the dark young lady did drop her handkerchief. And I rushed to pick it up.

I rushed—yes, still staggering under Honeybubble's blow, I rushed. But Honeybubble with his confounded gallantry—Honeybubble with his infernal goodness of heart—Honeybubble the athlete—Honeybubble was before me !

IV

MEETS HIS MATCH

From the moment that Mr. Honeybubble first ' cottoned to me ' I longed that he should meet and be attracted by some passenger more worthy of his steel, that I might myself retire into private life. There must surely, I thought, among so many passengers be somebody aboard who could give him bore for bore, so to speak, and enjoy it.

But, curiously enough, when this great thing happened, when the man was found and I could have had at least an hour off, I was so fascinated by the spectacle that I lingered, a willing victim, to see these giants engage, as it were, across my body.

The man was an American citizen, though so little like the Americans I know and admire, and so much like a parody American, that at first I thought he must be pretending. But I believe him to be real. He had a voice like a saxophone, and perhaps it was Honeybubble's voice, which is like a circular saw, that attracted him; for he entered that wilderness which Honeybubble had already created about him in the smoking-room and asked if one of us would make a fourth at Bridge with Colonel Philpott and another. Honeybubble had told me the previous day that he scarcely knew the rules of Bridge, but with his innate goodness of heart said he was willing to oblige. While they were waiting for the other two to appear the American sat down and talked.

'My name's Rooney,' he said, 'Ezra P. Rooney, of Chicago.'

'You're an American, sir?' said Honeybubble intelligently.

'Yes, sir, I'm an Amurrican citizen.'

'My name's Honeybubble. This is my friend, Mr. Haddock.'

'Glad to know you, Mr. Honeybubble. Mr. Haddock, I'm vurry pleased to make your acquaintance.'

'How d'you do, sir?' I said—and a sadly feeble response it sounded.

'It's very foggy outside,' said Honeybubble.

It was then that Mr. Rooney let fall the remark which showed me he was a match for Honeybubble— a perfect match. The fog was, in fact, dense. The *Cecic* had been steaming slow for two or three hours, scarce moving, with a prolonged blast of the siren every two minutes; so that every one on board was nearly mad with it, coming as it usually did half-way through a man's favourite joke.

' Yes, sir,' said Mr. Rooney, ' it's vurry thick. But we have a vurry careful Captain. Our Captain, sir, is a man that knows his business. You see how it is, sir,' he went on solemnly, as one explaining a difficult point to a child. ' It seems to you, maybe, as how we're wasting time, moving the way we are. But you'll understand, if our Captain was to go right ahead in this fog and another vessel was to cross our bows, by God, sir, we'd have a collision.'

He shook his head gravely, as if to let this sink in. And then they settled down to bore each other. Neither of them, I gladly found, took the smallest notice of me.

I must say that Honeybubble, true to his kindly character, did make some pretence of keeping it a conversation, and even of being interested in what the other fellow said. But Rooney was guilty of no such insincerity. He looked on Honeybubble entirely as a target—mere word-fodder.

' I've often wondered,' said Honeybubble, ' whether it wouldn't be possible to get rid of fog at sea by firing off big guns. A friend of mine who was in the War—a colonel he was, Colonel Bates—no, that wasn't his name—bless me, I'll forget my own name next. Well, it's of no consequence—yes, Bates it was, Colonel Bates—and he told me that there was never any fog in Flanders in the middle of a battle whatever there might be at the beginning, if you understand me. Now, it seems to me that if they were to apply that notion to the sea——'

' That's a vurry remarkable speculation,' said Mr.

Rooney, and instantly dismissed it from his mind.
' I noticed a lot more women smoking in public in
London.   I don't know how it strikes you, gentlemen,
but it seemed to me that more women had cigarettes
hanging out of their faces than they did last Fall
when I was over.   And I'm not going to conceal from
you, gentlemen, that I don't like to see it.'

Mr. Rooney was puffing at a huge cigar.

' My mother smokes,' said Mr. Honeybubble surprisingly.   ' And, what I always say——'

The siren, blasting terribly, concluded the remark.

' Well, sir, that's a vurry interesting point of view,'
retorted Rooney, not waiting to hear what Honeybubble
always said.   ' Maybe your mother's a nervous woman,
and it's no concern of mine how Mrs. Honeybubble
conciliates her nervous system.   But I have two
daughters and they don't smoke any.   In the United
States, sir, we put our women on a pedestal, and, by
God, sir, we expect them to stay on it.'

' What I always say,' said Honeybubble, going back
easily to where he was before, ' is, let them smoke in
the home if they must, but when they're in a public
place—well, it's a different thing entirely ; or, if it
isn't, it ought to be.   That's my opinion, and I think
you'll find it's the opinion of the majority of English-
men, though, of course, we can only speak for ourselves,
all of us.   What do you say, Mr. Rooney ? '

' I had a very poor night last night,' said Mr. Rooney,
as if Mr. Honeybubble's remarks had never been ; and
he yawned expansively to emphasize the poorness
of the night.   ' A vurry poor night indeed.   It's a
vurry curious thing, gentlemen, I never seem to sleep
so well on the starboard side of a boat.   Put me on

the port side of any steam-vessel you like to name, Amurrican or British, and I'll register my nine hours as easy and peaceful as a young child. But when you see me located on the starboard side, Mr. Honeybubble, you can be durned sure that I'm tossing and turning in that bunk till four or five every morning of the transit. Now how do you account for that, gentlemen?'

'I dare say it's something to do with the ship's motion,' suggested Mr. Honeybubble readily, not caring how he accounted for it as long as he got the lead in his hand. 'It's funny you should mention that, Mr. Rooney,' he went on quickly, 'because as I was saying to Mr. Haddock this afternoon there was a lot of running and trampling on the deck last night, right over my head—the sailors, I suppose; I don't know if you found the same. Well, as I was saying to Mr. Haddock, it isn't as if this was a cargo boat, one could understand it then, but with a lot of first class passengers trying to get to sleep it's a wonder people are not more considerate. And could I get off, Mr. Rooney? Not if you'd offered me a fortune. Well, I did as I always do; I got out of bed and sponged the back of my neck—that's a very old remedy my father taught me—I got into bed again, I put my pillow under the knees, and *that* was no use—well, what did I do then?'

Mr. Honeybubble paused but an instant for breath, and Mr. Rooney, who for some time had been showing signs of impatience, said immediately:

'I'm reading a vurry inspiring volume at the present time, Mr. Honeybubble: the Life and Enthoosiasms of Hercules B. Podd, late Chairman of the New York City and Federal Philanthropic Alliance. Now there, gentlemen, you had a man of big ideals, big, lovely, juicy, cracker-jack ideals ; a man of the people, sir ; a man that had his cultivated side, but above all, sir, a man that stood for ideals, a man that put country before party, sir ; ideals was his life, ideals was his eat and drink ; a man, Mr. Honeybubble, who stood by the Democratic Party till the bosses stabbed him in the back ; a man, Mr. Honeybubble——'

I saw Honeybubble open his mouth to explain, I imagine, what further steps he had taken to correct his sleeplessness. And then the battle became too much for me, I suppose ; I must have sunk into some swoon or slumber. For after that I heard nothing more very clearly. Outside in the fog the siren blared each minute, shaking the ship, and within those voices, not less vibrant, sounded interminably. Between the two combatants I lay in a fitful dream, as wearied soldiers sleep upon a battlefield and hear the shots fly over.

Stray disconnected fragments from the conflict penetrated my mind, such as :

' Yes, sir, you may take it from me the continent of Yurrup is in a vurry unsettled condition.'

' . . . things are very different to what they were twenty years ago. . . .'

' The man's not living that's going to stand for that bunk twice in a lifetime.'

' The last time over we saw an iceberg.'

' No, sir, I never cared for SHAKESPEARE. . . .'

Hours later (it seemed) I woke and found the Colonel and his friend beside us in the act of apologizing for keeping the table waiting.

' Colonel, it's of no consequence,' said Mr. Rooney,

' say no more. Mr. Haddock and his friend here have entertained me with a little discussion on politics and literatoor.'

Honeybubble that evening informed me that he liked Mr. Rooney, but found him a little tedious, and in his opinion, Mr. Rooney had an irritating voice.

And when I ran into Mr. Rooney next day he said: ' He's a rich talker, sir, your friend, Mr. What-is-it, but, gosh, he's no hand at listening ! '

V

IS SCURVILY TREATED

' AND what, gentlemen,' said Mr. Honeybubble, ' am I to do with that ? '

With these words Mr. Honeybubble amazingly drew from the tail-pocket of his tail-coat a quart bottle of whisky, placed it on the table before us and looked from face to face defiantly.

' Now that, sir,' said Mr. Rooney very distinctly yet with a certain effort, ' is a vurry remarkable circumstance.'

It was the last night of the voyage ; to-morrow the ship would wake up in quarantine off Staten Island. Already we were in American waters and the bar had been closed ; but before it closed Mr. Rooney and others had done their loyal best to ensure that as little as possible of the contaminating liquor should be carried into American waters, whether under seal or not. We sat now, four or five of us, in the smoking-room, round a table on which there were glasses, water-jugs and mineral waters, but nothing worse,

and discussed Prohibition. Then in comes Mr. Honeybubble of all people and produces a quart bottle of
whisky.

He had confided in me already that he had this
portent hidden in the famous green bag. He seldom
'took anything,' and did not understand casual
drinking, but he did like to have something by him
for moments of fatigue or an occasional nip or nightcap
before bed; and such had been his privations on his
last trip, he told me, and such was his inborn love of
liberty, that he had determined on this occasion to
become a smuggler. Even then, though, I had felt
the struggle proceeding in his breast between his
hereditary love of liberty and his hereditary dislike
of being found out. And the nearer the ship came to
the fatal shores the less free and the more fearful
beat the loyal heart of Mr. Honeybubble. The bottle
had begun to frighten him, and now, it appeared, he
had taken to carrying it about. He was, it was clear,
in an extreme state of nervous indecision.

We all stared at the bottle.

'Pardon the impertinence,' said Mr. Rooney,
'but is that article intended for importation or for
consumption on the high seas?'

'To tell you the truth, Mr. Rooney,' said Mr.
Honeybubble self-consciously, 'I was thinking of
taking it ashore. But I'm wondering now whether
perhaps I hadn't better throw it overboard.'

A sort of shiver, an inarticulate protest, ran round
the party; but we respected Honeybubble's scruples,
and only Rooney spoke.

'Now that's a vurry debatable prahposition,' he
said gravely, 'and, speaking for myself, the answer is

B

emphatic in the negative. Mind you, I don't say that many good citizens haven't jettisoned their liquor to salve their consciences in these waters, but I wouldn't say those gentlemen were objectionably red-blooded, Mr. Honeybubble, and I never heard of a hundred per cent Britisher who went so far. No, sir, not any.'

' Oh, of course, I'm not *afraid*,' said Honeybubble valiantly. ' It's the principle of the thing——'

He glanced timorously about the smoking-room and, though not afraid, dropped a newspaper over the naked bottle.

' *Principle* ? ' roared Rooney tremendously, swelling his chest. ' And what's the first principle and institootion of your great country, Mr. Honeybubble ? Answer me that.'

Honeybubble, quailing before the pointing finger, stuttered nervously. ' It's—er—it's—oh, well, it's law and order, I suppose.'

' Law and order hell, Mr. Honeybubble ! ' said Rooney contemptuously. ' Liberty was the institootion I had in mind. *Liberty, sir.*'

' Liberty,' repeated Honeybubble, much impressed. ' That's true. Of course it's awful nonsense all this——'

' Mr. Honeybubble,' said Rooney, more gravely than before and with his eye on the bottle, ' where is the man who has the right to say to you, a free-born Britisher : '' Throw that piece of your property into the ocean ? '' Does that man breathe, Mr. Honeybubble ? '

' He does not,' the Briton replied. ' Oh, no ; I shall certainly take it ashore. I'll see 'em damned

before they stop me.' And with these brave words
he seized the guilty bottle and was evidently proposing
to return it to his tail-pocket.

At this sight the eyes of Mr. Rooney started from
his head.

' One moment, sir,' he said quickly, holding up his
hand. ' Now don't misunderstand me, Mr. Honeybubble. I wouldn't like to have you say that Ezra
P. Rooney had handed you out a bunch of trouble.'

' Trouble ? D'you think I'll have trouble ? ' said
Honeybubble less bravely.

' Well, not if they don't catch you with the goods,
of *course*, Mr. Honeybubble. But——'

Mr. Rooney finished with a shrug suggestive of
nameless possibilities.

' What—what if they do ? ' quavered Honeybubble.

' Well, sir, you're not forgetting that this is an
offence against the enlightened constitootion of my
great country. This is no girls'-play, Mr. Honeybubble ; I've known men languish in the city jail for
half what you've got in that bottle. There was a
Britisher taken off a boat in New York Harbour last
fall and sent to Ellis Island, and died there. Yes,
sir.'

At these vivid pictures Mr. Honeybubble paled a
little.

' Is that a fact ? ' he said.

' Yes, sir.'

' Oh, well,' said Honeybubble vaguely, ' it's not
worth—— I think, perhaps, I'll throw it overboard
and have done with it.'

A slight cloud passed over Mr. Rooney's face, but
with an effort he controlled himself and said :

' Now don't get fanatical, Mr. Honeybubble. There's no need to go to extremes. See here, you'll need to have a *little* of it with you for your health, and mind you, in these days, supplies being what they are, the man that goes ashore with his hip-pocket absolootely dry is no true friend of the Amurrican people.'

' Then you think—— ? ' said Honeybubble, bewildered. ' But I thought you said—— The hip-pocket ? Is it safe ? '

' The hip-pocket's not made,' said Mr. Rooney, coming out into the open at last, ' that will look natural and law-abiding with a bottle of those dimensions, Mr. Honeybubble. But, sir, you don't have to take the *whole* bottle ashore.'

A pleased expression lightened the faces of all present as it seemed that the core of the position was at last made clear. But Honeybubble still looked bewildered.

' Get your daughter,' continued Mr. Rooney patiently, ' to give you a couple of scent-bottles, or throw away your cough-mixture and substitoot an emergency ration of the wine of Caledonia, Mr. Honeybubble, and the PRESIDENT himself won't touch you. Get me, Steve ? '

' I see,' said Honeybubble brightly. ' And pour away the rest of it ? '

Mr. Rooney sighed heavily, and for a moment I thought that he would abandon the struggle. But he said at last :

' Well, Mr. Honeybubble, that's as you please, but I dare say there's one or two gentlemen here would be willing to save you the exertion of a walk across the deck, if you prefer it. It so happens that I have in my pocket the vurry instrument that seems to be

desiderated,' and, taking from his pocket a corkscrew
he proceeded without further ado to operate on Mr.
Honeybubble's bottle.

'I see what you mean,' said Honeybubble, to the
general satisfaction. 'But is it allowed?' he went
on, with an anxious glance about the room.

'Well, sir,' said Rooney, 'we won't invite the
Captain to join us, and we won't shout for the chief
steward. Aside from any indiscretion of that nature
I don't know that any gentleman here is going to be
arrested. So here's to our friend Mr. Honeybubble
and the Eighteenth Amendment to the Constitootion
of the United States of Amurrica!'

Together, but silently, we drank this toast.

'Oh, well,' said Honeybubble, beaming, 'if you'll
take the responsibility, Mr. Rooney——'

'We will all take a little responsibility,' said Mr.
Rooney, helping himself to another ; 'and not much
soda.'

'Prohibition,' he continued richly at length, 'is a
vurry remarkable experiment in the spiritual uplift of
a great people, and of incalculable benefit to the toiling
masses of our cities. And I am surprised,' he went on,
draining his glass for the second time—' I am shocked,
Mr. Honeybubble, that you should have contemplated
setting your face against the onward march of ideals
to the extent of a whole quart bottle of Scotch—a
whole quart! Fill up, gentlemen——'

'Oh, but——' Honeybubble began.

'Fill up, gentlemen,' said Rooney, ignoring him,
'and remember the penalties provided by law for the
miscreant detected in the importation of liquor.
Remember, gentlemen, you stand between our brother

Honeybubble and the horrors of incarceration. Don't spare yourselves, boys ! '

Fired by this noble appeal for another we again charged Honeybubble's glass and afterwards our own.

Proceedings from then on became a little wild. Mr. Rooney grew more and more eloquent and dignified, and positively maudlin in his anxiety to save Mr. Honeybubble from trouble at the Customs. That gentleman, on the other hand, grew more and more free and fearless and quite contemptuous of laws. His courage rose as the whisky fell ; the more he drank the more was he prepared to smuggle, till, when the bottle was all but dry, he talked glibly of going ashore with gallons. And finally, when it became clear that Mr. Honeybubble would not be put to any trouble whatever, I remember Mr. Rooney seized the empty bottle and, remarking: 'We will now consign this incriminating vessel to the deep,' led us all out into the night.

Right ahead was a bright light. We marched in procession three times round the deck, Mr. Rooney singing.

And at last he turned and cried aloud: 'Say, Honeybubble, yonder stands the Statoo of Liberty. And right above it I see the sky-sign: " JAHN P. HONEYBUBBLE —HOSIER AND SMUGGLER ! " ' and solemnly he cast Mr. Honeybubble's bottle into the wine-dark sea.

Then—an unkind cut, I thought—he drew from his hip-pocket a substantial flask, well-filled, and he said: ' Those, Mr. Honeybubble, air the approximate dimensions of the vessel which I had in mind. Get one. Good night to you.'

And with these words he went to bed.

LITTLE TALKS

I

THE SEDATIVE

IT was about midnight, and all was quiet in the hospital. Nothing sounded except the continuous yowling of two cats outside my window, the puffing and blowing of steam-engines at the railway station, the flapping of a blind, the ringing of the telephone-bell in the hall, the singing of revellers in the street, the occasional arrival of a doctor at the front door, and the banging of a shutter in the basement. In spite of this hush I could not sleep. It was about two hours since the last nurse had tucked me up and left me, with my electric bell-push hidden handy under the pillow. To-night, if possible, I was to do without a sleeping-draught, for I was convalescent and must begin to throw off the bad habits of the invalid. But if I could not sleep I was to ring for the night nurse and she would give me hot milk or some stronger soporific. I extracted the bell-push and pushed it, and as usual the bell did not ring. I pushed the push at intervals for half an hour and nothing happened. The cats howled, the door banged, the locomotives hooted, the blind flapped, and I lay in my bed forlorn, without an appendix and with not much hope.

And then in the passage I heard the patter of healing feet. I uttered a hoarse but ineffective cry; it seems that most of the vocal organs are seated in the appendix, and so are the sneezing, coughing, nose-blowing and laughing organs, for whenever I do these simple things it hurts ; at any rate my cry was futile, so I picked up *Sunflowers*, the detestable novel my good aunt gave me, and I flung *Sunflowers* at the door.

It hurt, but I hit the door, and the night nurse came in. I told her I could not sleep, and she said I was not trying. I told her I wanted dope, but she said I must try to do without it. I said in that case she must stay for a little and compose my mind with soothing conversation. So she stood in front of the fire and we had soothing conversation.

I said : ' How is the Abdominal in Number 17 ? '

(I must explain that this is a very secretive hospital in which the staff have a strict and no doubt admirable code of reticence. I have asked from time to time, not in vulgar curiosity but by way of conversation, about the names and diseases of my fellow-sufferers in the building, but it seems that we are all anonymous, the one to the other. So that I know the others only by their room numbers and their generic complaints. They have neither name nor title nor sex ; they are the Abdominal in Number 17, or the Tubercular in 8, or the Pneumonia in Number 10, or the Child with Tonsils upstairs. And I am referred to, I believe, as the Emergency Abdominal in 21.)

The night nurse said that the Abdominal in 17 had had haemorrhage and nearly died during the afternoon, and she asked me if I felt like sleep yet. I said ' Not very,' so we talked about operations, with special reference to abdominals. I asked her about my appendix, and she said I had had a nice fat appendix and if it had not come out when it did it would have burst, and then I should have had peritonitis, with tubes, and she explained how very few people are quite the same again after that ; and I felt more and more like sleep. She gave a little demonstration with her fingers of the dimensions of my appendix ; she compared it with other appendices she had known and placed it finally for size and interest between the appendix of an elderly bishop and the appendix of a young Hungarian who had afterwards committed suicide ; and then we had a really jolly talk about insides, because I felt that, if I heard much more about insides, I should almost certainly drop off into a dreamless slumber.

Well, it turned out that in the best abdominal operations they take out the whole of the inside and leave it about outside while the surgeon is cutting up the particular bit he is interested in ; but they put pads of hot saline over the inside to keep it warm, and when it is all over he just bundles the inside back, like some one packing a suit-case in a great hurry ; and the night nurse said that really sometimes she wondered something wasn't packed upside down or the wrong way round.

So I asked, just casually and as a matter of academic interest, how much of my inside had been taken out, and she said not very much, and as far as she knew it was all put back in the right order and with no kinks. And she said there was really nothing in it, because she remembered the case of a very fat abdominal whose inside came out all over again after the operation because he was so fat, and the other nurse said : ' This case has collapsed ' ; so she went in, and there was his inside lying about the bed, so she said : ' What does

one do in a case like this, I wonder ? ' and the other
nurse said : ' Get some hot saline,' so they put hot
saline over the inside and kept it warm, and they took
the abdominal back to the ' theatre ' (which is what
they call the place where they do these things, which
I think is so nice), and the surgeon came and put the
inside back and the fat abdominal was as well as you
or me after it all, so you can see there is nothing in it.

After this little story the night nurse asked if I
was ready to sleep yet, and I said I didn't think I was
quite ready for sleep, not just yet, and if I did I thought
I might dream a little perhaps. So she said, did I
walk in my sleep, because last night she thought she
heard some one banging about the hall about two
o'clock in the morning. And I said that as a matter
of fact I did walk in my sleep sometimes, and for all
I knew it was me banging about in the hall. And
she said I ought to be careful, because she knew a man
once who walked in his sleep at the sea-side and jumped
over a cliff, and after that he was never the same
man again. Then she said I really must go to sleep,
and she would fetch me some hot milk ; and I lay and
brooded over our conversation.

And while she was away there was a great com-
motion in the hall, and the front door was opened and
shut several times. When she came back at last
I asked her what was the matter, and if another
Emergency Abdominal had come in, or what. She
said : ' No, it is only a B.I.D.,' and I said : ' What is a
B.I.D. ? ' and she said a B.I.D. was a Brought-in-
Dead, which means the victim of a street accident who
dies on his way to hospital.

This depressed me so much that I could hardly

drink my hot milk, and I said that I really thought, after all, perhaps I had better have a sleeping-draught. She said ' Very well,' and gave me a cachet the size of an oyster which stuck in my throat ; and while I was trying to get it to go one way or the other she picked up *Punch* and saw my initials, and she murmured ' " A. P. H."—how funny ! That's " Ante-Partum-Haemorrhage." ' Then she tucked me up and went away, bless her ; and after some time I went to sleep ; but it is no use my describing my dreams because the publisher would not print them, and even a psycho-analyst might not enjoy them. And now I do not know that I am quite so keen as I was on signing myself as I do, for haemorrhage was never one of my favourite words, and I am much less proud of being A. P. H.

II

THE WASH; OR, DAWN IN HOSPITAL

I WOKE like a log, one eye at a time.   Dimly I perceived beside my bed the night nurse, a basin of water in one hand, a thermometer in the other.

' Do you feel like a little wash now ? ' she said brightly.

' No, Nurse, I do not,' I said, and I went to sleep again.

When I re-woke (as the films say) there was a thermometer in my mouth, and the night nurse had ' captured ' (as the poets say) one of my hands.

' You know very well,' I said, taking out the ther-mometer, ' that my pulse and my temperature are always the same. I am very well. All that I need is sleep, and this is the hour of all hours in the day when I sleep the best. And if I am not to sleep I will not be washed.'

' You must be washed,' she said, ' before the doctor comes.'

' I am quite clean enough for a doctor,' I said. ' I will be washed at noon, when I stop sleeping.'

' You will be washed now,' she said, and, untucking all my snug bed-clothes, she piled them in a disorderly and draughty heap on my legs.

' This is barbarous,' I said.

' Shut the eyes,' said the night nurse, and scrubbed my face with a hard rubber sponge.

' It is extraordinary,' I said. ' Whenever the doctor comes he inquires if I have slept well; when Sister comes in she asks anxiously how I slept; last night you gave me, yourself, *two* different preparations or drugs to make me sleep. One would think that the whole establishment had no other aim than to make me sleep; all the resources of medicine have been mobilized to make me sleep. Yet when I do sleep, or rather when at last I drop into a fitful doze, I am immediately woken up. And for what purpose ? To be washed ! '

' Quite a martyr, aren't you ? ' she said. ' Now the hands.'

' The hands do not want washing,' I said. ' Wash the hands if you must ; but you will have no assistance from me.'

She dropped the hands into a basin of boiling water.

' I should have thought that you, at least, Nurse, would have seen the futility of these proceedings,' I

said.   'That sleeping-draught you gave me was wholly
ineffective.   All night I tossed upon my sleepless
couch, counting the hours, and every quarter reviling
the punctual clanging of your local clock.   Before
five, I know, I did not sleep a wink.   About six I
may have dropped off.   And no sooner do I drop off
than you wake me with thermometers and soap.'

'You have been sleeping like a log since ten o'clock.'
she said.   'Now the legs.'

'I deny it,' I said.   'What time is it now?'

'It's half-past seven,' she said, 'and I'm late.'

'Do you realize,' I said, 'that when I am in full
health I do not begin to *think* of washing till about nine,
and even then it does not always happen?   Yet
now, when I am extraordinarily ill and cruelly deprived
of my appendix, I am expected to endure this distasteful
ordeal at daybreak.'

'You're lucky,' she said; 'at some places they
wash the bodies at six.'

'No one shall wash *this* body at six,' I said.

'Can you lift that leg?'

'I can not,' I said; 'I am very ill.'

She went out of the room, and I went to sleep
again.

She came back with Nurse Andrews.   They woke
me up again and seized the right leg.   They soaped
the right leg and sponged it with a cruel sponge.
They put the right foot in a basin, poured methylated
spirit over the heel and sprinkled powder over the whole.
They rubbed the right leg with a towel and hid it
under a blanket.   Then they unveiled the left leg
and started on that.   Meanwhile the maid came in
and did the grate, leaving the door open.

' Do you have many deaths in this hospital ? ' I said.

' Not so many,' said the night nurse.

' Well, one of these days you will have an Abdominal dying of ablutions.   Just because I have no appendix,' I said, ' you think you can humiliate and torment me how you like. And there's another extraordinary thing I've discovered. I have been lying in this bed for a fortnight, Nurse, with no tobacco, no alcohol, no late nights, no night-clubs nor dances, nor the pernicious society of your sex, Nurse. I have not so much as eaten a sweet. I have lived, in fact, a life of abstinence and virtue, gazing at flowers, reading good books and eating little but vitamins. And if there is anything in what the reformers of this world tell us, I should wake each morning as fresh as a lark, Nurse. As soon as my eyes are open, I should have all my faculties alert and buoyant, ready for anything. Well, they are not, Nurse. I am not fresh. I wake each morning feeling like an old piece of blotting-paper, as other men do. I wake fuddled and suicidal and quarrelsome and hog-like, as usual. I wake like chewed string. I wake as I might wake after a week's debauch.'

' If you will turn him over, Nurse Andrews,' she said, ' I will do the back.'

' You will kindly leave the back alone,' I said. ' And I will not be talked about as if I were something in a butcher's shop. I am a living soul, with aspirations and a future life, and you are not to keep speaking of *the back* and *the leg*—as if I were so many joints of beef.'

Neither of the ministering angels took any notice of this protest, so I resumed the main argument.

'There is this further consideration,' I said. 'So far (touching wood) I have made a most rapid recovery from the mutilations of the doctors. The wound is not septic, the tongue is clean, and, if all goes well, as you have told me, I shall escape from your clutches in record time. In fact, Nurse (making every allowance for the skill and attention of the medical and nursing professions), the conclusion is that, in order to be healthy, and especially before an operation, a man should constantly absorb in enormous quantities all those poisons which modern civilization has made available, for this it is my habit to do, and you see the result ; but you will find that long after I leave you the teetotallers and vegetarians and non-smokers will be stretched upon their beds about this hospital, feebly complaining and constantly ringing the bell. Which is the worst case here, Nurse ? '

'The Abdominal in Number 9,' she said.

'An archdeacon, I believe. A non-smoker ? '

'Yes.'

'And a teetotaller ? '

'Yes.'

'Well, there you are,' I said.

'Now the teeth,' she answered.

I washed the teeth under protest, for this is a thing I hate to do before ladies. I then shaved by numbers and lay back exhausted. They then began the painful and fatiguing process which is known as making the patient comfortable. This took a quarter of an hour. I am condemned for some reason to sit upon an air-cushion, and while one is being washed one slides to the bottom of the bed. The two good women with heroic efforts hauled me up into a sitting position, but left the air-cushion behind. While the air-cushion was being placed in position I slid down the bed again ; it seemed to be a downhill bed. They heaved me on to the air-cushion, reviling me alternately for exerting myself too much and for making myself too heavy. When I was enthroned on the air-cushion at the right elevation the air-cushion was not central, and while the air-cushion was being centralized I slid down the bed again. When both the body and the air-cushion were right the pillows were wrong, and while the pillows were being put right, I did an avalanche, air-cushion and all. And all the time, with little anecdotes about abdominal cases they had known, the thoughtless women made me laugh, which hurts more than anything.

' Are you comfortable *now* ? ' said the night nurse at last.

' I am not,' I said. ' But I would rather live on in discomfort than perish of exhaustion in a position of ease. I do not feel nearly so well. For a whole hour, Nurse, I have had worry and hard work, and all this before breakfast. When a man is in health, Nurse, a man takes great care of himself before breakfast, husbands his strength, nurses his soul and does as little as possible. But here upon a bed of sickness he does the equivalent of about two hours' hard labour before breakfast. It's extraordinary. And speaking of breakfast, Nurse—well, what about breakfast ? '

The night nurse arranged upon the table a number of nasty-looking steel instruments.

' The doctor is coming before breakfast,' she said, ' to take your stitches out. And,' she added wickedly, ' I hope it hurts.'

KATE IN THE CALL-BOX

' WELL, I suppose she's gone to sleep in there, that's all, dear. Some people don't *think*, do they? What's the time, dear? Seven already? They'll tear me to pieces when I get back. Well, I shall count ten and if she's not out of it by then I'll bang on the glass if I go to prison for it. One—two—three—four—five—— Oh, snakes! I can't wait any longer. There!—Not so much as a look—didn't turn round even. Well, you see me give her a look when she does come out. Christmas! will she never stop talking? Nobody can't have all that to say, not if she's got off with a bishop, and I wouldn't put it past her—well, look at the hat, dear. *That's* no milk-and-water conversation, *I'll* swear. Actress, I dare say and running off with a Member of Parliament—choosing a train to Brighton, I shouldn't wonder. Well, there's nothing against that if she don't keep respectable people spoiling their shoe-leather outside. Glory, she's done! You'll come inside, dear, won't you? I'm a born fool with the telephone. Well, would you believe it, she's begun again. " Farewell, Fortescue, and be sure to bring your dress-suit ! " That's right, don't hurry, drop your bag, and powder your nose, and read the notices twice over, there's no one waiting. Here she comes. Now see me give her a look. No, Madam, not at all—a pleasure, I'm sure ! '

' Well, here we are. Shut the door tight, dear. My dear, the scent ! That woman washes in it. You put the pennies in, dear, and then I'll have a witness. I don't trust these things no farther than I can see them,

and that's not far. Hullo? Hullo? 12856 Padding-
ton. Well, I said it clear enough. 12856 Paddington.
Got the pennies ready? Of course if he's not there I
don't know what's going to happen. Hold my hand,
dear, I'm all of a dither. Hullo? Quick, dear, put
two pennies in and turn the handle. Yes, it *is* " One."
Now the other. And that's Two. Hullo? Hullo?
Is that Paddington 12856? Is that Mrs. Rigby's?
Is that you, Fred? Hullo? Well, it's like this,
Fred, I can't come out to-night, you see—— Hullo?
I'm sorry, Fred, but Mrs. Mortimer's got a party, you
see, and Mabel's got the whooping-cough or something.
I told her about your sailing in the morning, but Mrs.
Mortimer said—— Hullo? What's that? Isn't
that Fred Mullins? Very sorry, sir, I'm sure, but I
thought you said you was. Well, what d'you think
of that? Lord Barley, if you please. Hullo, Miss?
Hullo? You give me the wrong number. Yes, I'm
sorry too. 12856 Paddington it is, and don't put me
on to the PRINCE OF WALES because I'm not dressed
for it. My dear, pouring out my heart to a strange
lord! I'm blushing all over. Spoke very civil too—
Hullo? It'll be WINSTON CHURCHILL next, I suppose.
Hullo? No, I will *not* put two pennies in, you've
had my money and you know it. Yes, I dare say.
Hullo? Is that Mrs. Rigby's? Is Mr. Mullins there?
Is that you, Fred? Fred? I say, Fred? I can't
come out to-night, Fred. Yes, I know, but it's no
good swearing, besides they'll charge extra. Well,
you see, Mrs. Mortimer's got a party, and she says
she can't let me go because Mabel's got the whooping-
cough, you see. I told her you was going to sea in
the morning, but she says she can't help that. Well,

she's in her rights; I had last night, you see, and it isn't my night by rights. Hullo? Yes, I know it's a shame, but there you are, what must be must—— Hullo? No, it's no good, Fred. She's a good old soul, really she is, and I can't leave her with nobody. Still, I did want to see you, Fred. What time's your train, Fred? No, there's the washing-up, you see. I'd never do it, not by then. No, it's good-bye now, Fred, and there's no getting away from it. How are you, Fred? Are you looking nice? Are you wearing the blue tie I give you, Fred? I wish I could see you, Fred. Hullo? Yes, Fred, of course I love you, Fred, only I can't say much, not here, because Maud's here with me, you see. Hullo? I said OF COURSE I LOVE YOU—— What? Hullo? Three more minutes? Yes, of course we'll have three more minutes, what d'you think? Make it four. What? *Oh!* More money, is it? Quick, Maud, give this blood-sucker two more pennies! One—(you count beautiful, Miss)—Two. Thank you, Maud. Hullo? Hullo? Fred? Well, here we are again. What? Yes, Maud's here, I told you. Why? What's the matter with *her*? Well, of course, if you want to be as private as all that—— Maud, dear, Fred says how are you? and would you think it rude if he said something in private like? No offence, dear; you know what I mean——'

'Well, now you've done it, Fred; she's gone off in one of her tantrums and took my purse with her. Oh, well, I'm glad reelly; it *was* a bit awkward with her in my pocket. Maud doesn't like you much, Fred. Oh, you knew that, did you? Well, well, this time to-morrow you'll be on the briny, I suppose. Oh, dear! Will you send me a Wireless, Fred, if it don't

cost too much—just "Thinking of you," Fred, or
something ? Well, one word would do, if it's a
good one—I'll know who it's from. What ? Elevenpence a word ? Oh, well, if I'm not worth elevenpence
there's no more to be said, of course. Hullo ? Will
there be any girls on the ship, Fred ? I'm glad of
that, Fred. D'you know what Maud said this afternoon ? She said she saw you at the pictures Friday
with another girl. I said that would be your sister,
Fred, but she said this girl had red hair. So I said
your sister very often wore a red wig Fridays, because
that's her day out. But Maud said this wasn't a
wig, so then we had words. Who was she, Fred ?
No, I don't want to know, not reelly ; I was only
teasing ; only last night you did say I was the only
one, didn't you ? and I thought perhaps—Hullo ? '

'I see. It's all right, Fred, it's a free country, isn't
it ? You've a perfect right to go to the pictures.
No, I'm not crying, Fred—not so's you'd notice.
Hullo ? How long will you be gone, Fred ? Six
months ? Oh, Fred, it's a long time, isn't it ? You
will take care with them Australian girls, Fred ?
They're an artful lot, I've always heard, specially
with sailors. Don't you have nothing to do with them,
dear—you've only got to say : " I've plighted my troth
to a girl called Kate," and then they'll leave you alone,
you see. Oh, well, I must be getting back, I suppose.
I wish it was last night, Fred. You'll think of me
sometimes, Fred—think of me washing up the dinner-
things and thinking of you, and I'll think of you
lashed to the mast and thinking of me, you see, and
then something's bound to happen.'

'Well, good-bye, Fred—you haven't said you love

me yet.   Go on, dear, what's the matter with you ?
They won't charge anything.   I don't believe you do,
Fred.   What about that ginger girl ?   " Golden," is
it ?   Oh, well, I beg her pardon, I'm sure.   Well, I
love *you*, Fred, and I don't care who's listening.
What'll you do to-night, Fred, before the train goes ?
Go to the pictures, will you ?   Oh ?   Well, I wouldn't
go to the pictures, Fred, if I were you, not to-night.
I dunno.   Well, I wouldn't like to think of you sitting
at the pictures while I'm washing up—not on your
last night.   I'd rather think you was moping somewhere
—all by yourself, Fred.   Oh, dear, I did want to see
you off, Fred.   Well, never mind ; what is six months
when all's said and done ?   You'll be back soon,
won't you ?   and then we'll get married.   Hullo ?
You *are* going to marry me, aren't you, Fred ?   Hullo ?
What ?   Three more minutes ?   Yes, of course.   Hullo ?
Hullo ?   Fred, you are going to marry me ?   Well, I
haven't got two pennies.   Can't you wait a minute ?
I say, Fred, Maud's gone off with the purse and I've
no more coppers.   You do love me, don't you, Fred ?
Hullo ?   Hullo ?   No, I haven't, and if you cut me
off, young woman, I'll tear your eyes out !   Fred ?
Fred ?   Are you there, Fred ?   Good-bye, Fred !   You
are going to marry me, Fred. . . .   Hullo ? '

   ' *Hullo ?* '

   ' Here, what's the game ?   You've cut me off !
Hullo ? '

      ' Fred ?   Are you there, Fred ? '

         ' Fred ? '

            ' *Fred ?* '

               ' FRED ? '

   ' Oh, dear. . . .'

IV

THE BARGAIN COUNTER

' THANK you, Madam ; pay at the desk, please. Good morning, Madam—My dear, what a crush ! Like flies, aren't they ? Well, my dear, I wanted to tell you, it's all up—Arthur and me, I mean. We had a scene last night, such a scene, well, scene's not the word—Cami-bockers ? No, Madam ; straight through and on the right—Don't hurry me, dear, I'm in such a state I can't hardly think. Well, Arthur came in last night, you see, and I could tell at once there was something in the wind because he was wearing his bowler, you see, and I told him long ago I didn't like him in his bowler, and he's never worn it since, not till last night, so I said, " The bowler, eh ? I suppose your passion's burnt itself out ? "—joking, you see—Boys' pants ? No, Madam, in the Juveniles, the next department—Well, he looked sheepish at that, like when you tell a man he's got no soul for music and he hasn't, and after a bit he said he was sorry, but the fact was, he'd come to say Good-bye, because if the truth was told he was going to be married. So I said, " Married, eh ? Congratulations, I'm sure, and what may her name be ? " Because I wasn't going to show anything, you see. " Well, if you want to know," he said, " her name's Sylvia Wilkins." And then he told me all about her, from her blasted eyes to her blasted address, which is Addison Road, if you please. Well, we were sitting in the front-room, you see, because it was raining, and just then Father comes along the passage, and Father's always said he'd horsewhip anybody if their intentions wasn't honourable—Father's very old-fashioned, you see—so when I saw Father I said—No, Mr. Arundale, I wasn't gossiping, I was just saying to Miss Williams, these Windsor night-gowns have all gone but six and it seems to me we're throwing them away at the price— Nasty little rat ! I'd be ashamed to be a shop-walker if I was a man!—So I said to Father, "Congratulate Arthur, Father, he's going to be married." " To you, my dear ? " says Father, all of a radio. " No," I said, " to Sylvia Wilkins." Well, you see, I've always let on to Father that me and Arthur were more or less engaged, because if I hadn't done that he'd have put his hoof down long ago—Girls' Outfits ? the next department, Madam—So when Father heard about Sylvia Wilkins, he saw scarlet, you see—well, I think he'd had one or two, and he said to Arthur : " Look here, young scum-of-the-earth, you've betrayed my daughter, and I'm goin' to horsewhip you, see ? " So I said Arthur hadn't betrayed me, and Arthur said he wasn't going to be horsewhipped—Ribbons, Madam ? Yes, Madam, straight through to the Fancy and Speci- alities—That young woman's buying half the shop, my dear, getting her trousseau I shouldn't wonder. I can't stand those sunflower shingles, can you ?— Well, so Father went into the kitchen to look for the horsewhip—Pyjamas ? Yes, Madam. Would it be for your personal wear ? Certainly. We are selling a great many of the Paris Pyjama—for camp and yacht- wear. Yes, Madam, they are very much worn. The heliotrope are very fetching, Madam. Or would you prefer the Cambridge blue ? One-three-ten, Madam, reduced from thirty-five shillings. We are practic- ally giving them away, Madam. Two pairs of the

Cambridge ? Very well, Madam. Cash, Madam, or on account ? Wonderful weather, Madam, quite a treat. A little fresher to-day, I think. Thank you, Madam. Will you pay at the desk, please? Good morning, Madam—Well, my dear, Father couldn't find the horse-whip, because Mother hid it the moment she heard him on the rampage, you see, but that only made him the madder, and he came back waving the coal-hatchet and shouting and swearing something terrible, and he said to Arthur, " Will you come out in the yard and be horsewhipped, young man ? " And Arthur said, " Not with a hatchet, sir," very polite, you see. Well, Father was mad at that, you see, and reelly I think he thought the hatchet was a horsewhip, so he lifted up the horsewhip, the hatchet, I mean—Yes, Mr. Arundale ? Miss Farrow, forward, bust-bodices, please—Well, Arthur never turned a hair, but I thought it was all up with him, but just then Mother came in, and she gave Father one of her suffering looks and she said, " Where did you put the aspirins, Tom, my head's splitting ? " Well, that seemed to sober Father, because he always says that Mother's headaches knock the stuffing out of him, so he put down the hatchet and Mother said, " What's the argument about ? "—Boys' underclothes ? Straight through to the Juveniles, Madam—You wouldn't think there were so many boys in the world, would you ? Where was I ? Oh, yes. Well, Arthur spoke up and he said he'd been gone on this Sylvia Wilkins for years, only she wouldn't have him, but she'd gone and changed her mind, you see, and he said he and me were very good friends but that was all. So I said, " That's right." Well, I'd have said anything to save a scene. So Father flared up and

he said, " Friends my eye ! Then what's all the kissing
and cuddling for, tell me that ! " My dear, wasn't
it awful ? Well, Mother said " Don't be vulgar, Tom ! "
And there's no getting away from it, Father *is* vulgar
when he's worked up. So he said, " Vulgar, am I ?
Well, will this young feller-me-lad answer a straight
question—has there been kissing and cuddling or has
there not ? " So Arthur said there might have been
a little kissing and cuddling, but only Platonic, you
see. Well, then the fat was in the fire. " Platonic ! "
shouts Father, " you dare to try those games with my
daughter ! " And he picks up the hatchet and he
makes for Arthur. Well, Mother caught hold of him
and I caught hold of him, and there was a regular
dog-fight, and the next thing I knew, there was Arthur
lying on the ground with the blood all over his face.
My dear, the blood ! You never saw anything like it
—Are you being attended to, Madam ? We have a
very cheap line in silk bed-socks to-day. Pardon ?
Cheese, Madam ? That will be in the Provisions,
through the Livestock. Thank you—" Well," says
Father, " is he dead ? " " Looks like it," Mother said.
" Well," says Father, " the first thing is to get rid of
the body, I won't have a scandal in *this* house," because
Father reads a lot of these murder stories, you see.
Well, Mother and me bathed Arthur's face, while
Father walked up and down thinking how to get rid
of the body. And reelly I did think Arthur was done
for, he lay so still. But presently he sits up, and it
was only a flesh-wound, so Father apologized and we
all had supper—Boys' pants ? Straight through to
the Juveniles, Madam—Well, that's the end of *my*
little romance—Night-gowns ? Yes, Madam. The

Windsor style is very attractive. All silk, hand-lace, as worn by the Queen of Serbia. We have them in the three shades, Madam, Rose du Barri, Cerise and Flesh. There has been a great run on this style, Madam. These are the last half-dozen, Madam. We are selling them at a very considerable reduction, Madam, twenty-six shillings, Madam, marked at two guineas. I will inquire, Madam—Mr. Arundale?— Yes, Madam, for that number we would let them go at half-price, Madam. Shall I send them? Certainly, Madam. The weather is wonderful, is it not, Madam? Quite a treat. A little fresher to-day, I think. And the name, please? Miss Sylvia Wilkins. Miss Sylvia *Wilkins*, did you say, Madam? And the address? 410, Addison Road. Thank you, Madam, I will have them sent by the next delivery. Will you pay at the desk, please? *Good* morning, Madam—Well, my dear, what d'you think of that? That's the little fairy that's ruined my life—and I've sold her six nighties for half-price!'

V

SIXPENNY DIPS; OR, THE DANCING PARTNER

(SCENE—*The Palais de Danse*)

' THERE they go, Maud, six of them after that Milly again. It beats me what a man sees in her—doesn't it you, dear? Well, there don't seem to be any ugly rush for you and me, Maud; here we are, left again. You and me's a pair of Cinderellas, that's what it is. Well, ugly ducklings if you like. Still, you'd think one of us was worth a tanner, wouldn't you? Oh, well, who'd be a dancing partner? Sixpence a time and no offers. I've had one dance to-night—*one*, my dear, would you believe it? And he was a hundred. I shall get this inferior complex they talk about. Well, that Lotty's booked for the evening night after night, an' if there's all that money flying about you'd think somebody might squander a sixpence in this direction. But oh, no, it's always the same—Milly and Lotty and Madge, and the rest nowhere.'

'Madge Elliot's sweetly pretty, I will say; but that Milly——! And, my dear, her *dancing*! Well, if I was a man I'd pay more money to dance with a sick cow. There she goes with her little lounge-lizard; she's welcome to that, I'm sure. Did you see the nasty look she gave us! Saucy cat! Who's getting excited, dear? Do you think I care? I never could stand this tune, anyway, hark at it, and I want to get on with my knitting, you see. There's little Madge. I know one thing—I wouldn't Black Bottom with a Jew-boy in plus-fours if he paid me half a crown. I wonder you don't bring some needlework too, dear; you spend as much time sitting in the shop-window as I do. No offence, Maud, but you don't draw much of a crowd yourself, do you, dear? Don't be unkind, dear; you've made me drop a stitch. A jersey? No, dear, it's a sock. A surprise for Albert. For his birthday, you see; I know he can do with some socks. Well, I'm glad Albert can't see me now, that's one consolation. If he saw me sitting here neglected like a snowdrop in the New Forest he'd have seventeen fits. Wild? Wild's not the word for it! That man

—he'd have me out of the place before you could say knife, contract or no contract. D'you think this looks like a man's size in socks, dear ? It looks to me more like something in the juvenile department.'

' Don't look up, but there's a boy got his eye on us. Maud, dear, I do believe one of us is about to click ! Now you can look, he's tying his shoe-lace. Poor darling ! first time out I should say. Just look at him preening and all of a-dither. Tying his tie now, you see. Isn't he a lamb ? I'm going to give him the gay glance, and chance it. Oh, gosh ! here he comes, ticket and all. What would his mother say ? It's me, Maud, I do believe——'

' Well, what d'you think of that ? Just took one look at me and he was off like a shot out of a gun. Am I such a sight as all that, Maud ? Mother used to say I was the beauty of the family. Well, I shall give up the dancing and go into Parliament, that's all I'm fit for, it seems. Lucky Albert didn't see that, he'd have knocked the boy down as soon as look at him. My dear, this tune gives me the pip. It's a pity they can't invent a white man's dance.'

' There's the old custard who fell for me, dear. Yes, that one ; looks like a balloon and dances like a Tank. My dear, he's a caution. P'raps I'm cut out to be an old man's darling. Well, he said, " Haw ! I've had my eye on you for a long time," he said. So I said, " Flattered, I'm sure." Then he said, " Haw ! you lead a gay life, don't you ? " " Gay ? " I said. " Well, I mean dancing every night and that," he said. " And afternoons too," I said. " Oh, yes, we *do* have a time ! " Then he said, " Haw ! you get a queer lot of partners, I dare say." " Some's

funnier than others," I said, because just then he
came down like a ton of bricks on my toe. "A
thousand apologies," he says. "One's enough," I
said. Then he said, "Can you give me any tips about
my dancing?" "A lesson's ten-and-sixpence," I
said. So he said as quick as you like, "Oh, well, we
won't bother; it's an education just to dance with
you." I said, "Well, hold me tighter, there's no charge
for that." "And keep your great stomach in," I
said, only I said it to myself. Well, my dear, we went
round that floor together like a whale and a whiting,
and at the end he was puffing like a steam-roller on a
hot day. "Haw! I'd like to have another," he said, so
I said, "You're welcome, I have the next free." So he
said, "Well, I'm sorry, I've got my wife here." Well,
I'm not going to be no snake in the grass, I thought,
so I held out my hand for the ticket and he laid hold
of it like the Sheik's Good-bye. So I said, "The
ticket, please!" And he said, "Haw! the ticket; I'd
like to keep that as a memento." So I said, "Well,
I have to hand it in for my commission, you see." So
he said, "Haw! Pity. Then it's *Au revoir*, perhaps."
So I said, "You never know, do you?" and we drifted
apart. And that's *my* evening's work up to date.'
  'My dear, this tune! Who's that? My dear,
if it isn't Albert! Well, did you ever? He hates
dancing. Wonders will never cease. . . . Albert!'
  'Well, Albert, where do you spring from? Glad to
see you, Albert, but what a surprise! I was speaking
of you only a minute gone—wasn't I, Maud? Oh,
sorry—Maud, this is my friend, Mr. Galloway. Miss
Percival—Mr. Galloway. Want to dance, do you?
Well, you'll have to have a ticket, Albert. Can't

dance with me without a ticket, you know, not if
you was Ivor Novello. Oh, you've got one, have
you ? Knows the ropes, don't he, Maud ? I'm quite
suspicious. Come on, then. Now then. One, two,
three, four. One, two, three, four. One, two, *one*
two. Not so bad. Sure I'm worth the sixpence,
Albert ? Then that's all right. Well, I can tell you
you're lucky to catch me free like you did, I've been
that busy this evening. I'd just that instant sat down
for a rest, the first minute's peace I've had since we
opened, and then you came in. Been quite a run on
me to-night, Albert, you'd be surprised.'

' Hold me tighter, dear, and don't hop. Oh, yes,
regular lads, all of them, specially one. I've had five
with him, Albert ; you would have been jealous.
Very good-looking, Albert, and dances like a duke.
Don't hop, dear. Quite young, well, twenty-five,
say—officer I should think. All over me, Albert.
Oh, well, they all were . . .'

' And that's that. Now give me the ticket.
Want another, Albert ? Well, I'll squeeze you in
if I can, somewhere. Yes, that's one of our girls.
Milly, her name is. Yes, Milly Potts. Hasn't been
here long. Want to dance with her, do you ? Don't
be silly ; why should *I* mind ? Oh, well, you've only
got to ask her. Like an introduction ? Oh, you
know her, do you ? That's funny, Albert. Fancy
you knowing Milly Potts, Albert ! You never told
me you knew Milly Potts, Albert. Old friends, eh ?
Oh, Putney, was it ? At the Palais, perhaps ? Oh,
yes, I heard she left there in a hurry. That's where
you picked up your dancing, I dare say. Yes, her's
is very much after your style, now I come to think

of it—hop, skip and fall down. Well, there you are, the band's starting. What are you waiting for? Go to it, Albert, and good luck to you, I'm sure! No, I won't be dancing no more to-night, I've pains in the back. Go on, Albert, or you'll miss the fairy. . . .'

' Well, Maud, here we are again, my dear, two minds with but a single thought, and no offers! If you ask me, that man came here after Milly Potts and nobody else, and if you want a gentleman's sock half finished here you are, because I've done with it . . . ! '

' Sorry, dear, did it hit you? But, I mean to say —Milly Potts . . . ! '

' Milly *Potts*! '

VI

LOVE'S BLISS; OR, WORKING HIM UP TO IT

' UNLUCKY again, Bill, I told you so, we've missed half of it. Well, never mind, I've seen it before, so I can tell you. " Love's Bliss," it's called, pretty name for a picture, isn't it? Can you see, Bill, because I can't—if I was that size I'd take a back-seat, wouldn't you, or wear a smaller size in hats. What's this, now? Oh, yes. Well, this man builds bridges, you see, and he's building a bridge over this ravine, only he gives way to drink, you see—d'you mind changing places, Bill, this hat's a knock-out. Thank you, Bill, that's better, well, he was married to a blonde in New York, you see, only she gave him the chuck —Lor, Bill, where's my bag? Poke about on the floor, Bill, will you? That's my foot, dear. Got

it ? What a mercy ! Well, that's why he gives
way to drink, you see—there you are—

DROWNING CARE IN INDULGENCE
BLAKE LOSES HIS GRIP

Funny sort of man, isn't he—one glance at a decanter
and he gets the staggers. There's the girl, you see
—that's Fay Martin, Bill—no, it isn't, that's the other
girl, and this is the cabaret where she dances, you see
—that's her, the dark one. Sweetly pretty, isn't she ?
She's gone on Blake, you see, only he's that blind he
don't notice ; he puts me in mind of you, Bill, rather
—you know, don't think enough of himself. Well, he's
brooding over the blonde, you see, and boozing in
between, only of course he don't love her really, it's
his wounded pride, you see, and this dark girl tries to
woo him from the bottle, like—there you are

CUT IT OUT, STRANGER

she says, and he says :

GIRLIE, YOU'RE A GOOD KID

No, he don't, that's later, he says :

HELL, QUIT BUMMING AROUND, CAN'T YOU !

There's the bridge, you see, isn't it a *height*, Bill,
and this is a rough night at the cabaret, all the lads
are after her, you see, and this man with the squint
wants to compromise her, that's Dago Dick, he's the
boss, sit over this way a bit, you'll see better. Well,
she won't have no truck with him because of Blake,
only of course she don't show nothing, Mabel said she
was a bit like me she thought, bottles up her feelings

and that. Would you believe it, Bill, I've dropped my bag again. That's my foot. You are a one, Bill, I do believe you do it a-purpose. Got it? Now you've missed the letter, I think, no, you haven't, there you are

BLAKE'S HAND LOSES ITS CUNNING

There he is with his plans, you see, and the bridge has gone cock-eye because of the drink, your hand's very hot, Bill, it don't matter, I like it. Now we *have* missed the letter. Well, it was from the President or somebody and it says the bridge don't meet in the middle or something, so Blake loses his job, and then he takes to drinking out of the bottle and that's always a bad sign, END OF PART TWO.'

' No, thank you, dear, but I could do with a chocolate; my *dear*, there's Mabel with Tom Higgins, I wondered who it was, she's had her head on his shoulder all the evening, well, I always say I like a man who's not ashamed of a little emotion, don't you? I dunno, Bill, they all look lovely, let's have that box with the blue ribbon—Thank you, Bill! Um! Um! Oh scrumptious! I've got a *nougat*! What's yours?'

' Well, here we are again, PART THREE. Blake's gone to the bad, you see, and drinks all the time, but this girl keeps her eye on him—there he is staggering into the snow, you see, pity, isn't it, he's a nice man, reelly—well, she follows him, there she goes, through the wood, you see—pretty, isn't it? I said, pretty isn't it, but this *nougat's* stuck to the roof of my mouth, I can't hardly talk. That's better. Well, he has a fit or something in the snow, you see, and she drags him to the hut and nurses him. D'you mind

c

changing hands, dear, I've got the cramp. That's
better. See if you can find me a coffee-cream—there
she is giving him milk, you see, isn't she sweet?

WEEKS PASS. Now he's a new man again, you
see, and the bridge don't get on without him, so he's
got the job again—Oh! I'm ever so sleepy—what's
that?

A BRAND PLUCKED FROM THE BURNING

That's Blake, I suppose—D'you mind if I rest my
head on your shoulder, Bill, I'm that tired—that's
better, only now I can't see—it don't matter, I
remember it—what's happening? Crying, is she?
Oh, yes—well she wants to marry him, you see, but
the only thing he seems to care about is this bridge,
because he's that blind, you see, and when she sees
the photograph—has she seen the photograph yet?
Well, in a minute she'll see a photograph of the blonde
under his pillow, and then she goes back to the cabaret
and goes gay again, because the bridge was bad
enough but the blonde is a knock-out. Is my hand
sticky, Bill? Well, then the bridge is finished and
Blake goes down to the cabaret to celebrate and Dago
Dick is trying it on with the girl, you see, and
she's that wretched she don't care *what* happens—
your hair smells nice, Bill, have you washed it or
what? So Blake comes in in the nick of time and he
knocks Dago Dick down—has he knocked Dago Dick
down yet? Well, in a minute you'll see Blake knock
Dago Dick down. Give me another choc, Bill, pop
it in my mouth, dear, I can't move—Ta! Well,
Blake still don't say nothing, the silly chump, and
then the blonde turns up from New York—have you

seen the blonde yet? Yes, a fair girl. Fluffy? Of *course*. Yes, that's the girl—she looks shallow, but she's deep reelly—well, the moment she sees Blake she knows he's gone on the dark girl, though he don't know it himself, so she runs up to the bridge to throw herself off—there she goes—that's so as to give him his freedom, you see—my *dear*, what a height, I'm giddy all over—there goes the other girl—well, didn't you see her face when she saw the blonde—she's going to throw herself over too, you see—there you are— THE GREAT SACRIFICE—and they're both doing it— seems silly, don't it?—there she is on the bridge, see her dropping a stone?—there it goes!—down, down— give me another choc, Bill—there's the rocks—*plop!* oh, dear—look at the wind in her skirt, Bill—now she's seen the blonde—they're struggling—each saving the other, you see—*right* on the edge—hold me tight, Bill, I can't bear it! Oh, they're over! what a *shame!* —give me a choc, dear—there she is, you see, swimming after the blonde—that's the dark girl—she bounced on a bush, you see, and was saved. Bringing in the body, you see—but it's no good, the blonde's a goner.'

' So Blake's eyes are opened at last, you see—see him biting his lips?—because if he'd only said something a bit sooner it wouldn't never have happened, you see—MORAL, keep your eyes open and never bottle up the feelings.'

' Look at 'em now—what a kiss!—you never kissed me like that, Bill—would you like to? Well, you can't. Why *not*? Why not, indeed. Well, for one thing they're going to be married, you see—and we aren't. Oh, we are, are we? First *I've* heard of it, I'm sure. Well, I dunno. Do you mean it? Do

you *reelly*, Bill ? Oh well, if it's *that* way—perhaps
I might, Bill. Of *course* I do ! How soon, Bill ?
Oh, sooner than that, Bill. No, of *course* you can't !
Not here, dear. I'm *shy*, Bill. Well, that's that.
Shall we go now, Bill ? '

VII

THE LECTURE

' WELL, Dad, what is it, Mum said you wanted me,
I suppose I'm in for another lecture—is that it ?—
you're looking like a low note on the saxophone,
darling, that's a sure sign, well, out with it, Dad,
and be matey about it, do, I'll sit on your knee, then
you can give it me between the eyes, can't you, darling,
well, what's the Great War about ? Tommy's party,
I suppose, I thought there might be words about
that, but don't you turn on the Modern Girl, Dad,
because I shall just dissolve into a swamp of girlish
tears, and you know what a sight I am crying, don't
you, that record's a dud, anyhow, the Modern Girl,
my dear, it's *mildewed*, the Modern Girl indeed,
how dare you sit there and lecture me about the
Modern Girl ? I know one thing, if Mum hadn't been
a Modern Girl you'd never have married her, would
you, old rip ? There wasn't much JANE AUSTEN about
you two, I know you, you and your shrubberies and
masks and things, I call it indecent, so don't say
another word about that, will you, darling, because I
couldn't bear it, what's all the *agitato* about this party,
anyhow, I know I came home with " now the rosy dawn
appearing," but what's the matter with the dawn,

darling, I always thought the dawn was absolutely It
with an intellectual like you, Dad, the only two bits
of poitry I know are all about the mouldy dawn, didn't
you and Mum get up and see the dawn, Dad, well,
we sit up and see it, that's the only difference, but it's
the old story, if a man sees the dawn it's poitry,
and if a woman sees it it's the Modern Girl, but if
you'd even seen Ludgate Hill at dawn you'd have
stayed up yourself, darling—so that's enough of that.'

'As for the party, well, of course we went to the
Colts and Fillies, where else is there to go to, and how
was I to know it would be raided, who in the world
would *think* of raiding such a club, my dear, it's like
the British Museum, they *simply* talk of nothing but
the Drama, and not so much as a cup of cocoa after
eleven o'clock, well, then the raid began, and really
it was quite a relief, because my head was simply
splitting with IBSEN and SHAW and all those perfectly
contagious people in Czecho-Slo-what-is-it, of course
half the policemen had been there for hours, behaving
too disgustingly, and if you call that English I don't,
I mean, crawling into a perfectly highbrow club in
sheep's clothing and dickies and everything, and
ordering vodka after hours, just *goading* people into
sin, that's all it is, and, if you ask me, they ought
to be prosecuted, so don't you stand up for them,
darling, or I shall just cut you out of my life.'

'And it's not true that Tommy knocked the Inspector down, all he did was to make a gesture of absolute
loathing, and the man fell down—simply a gesture,
darling, that was all, and I know what I'm talking
about, because at the time I was blowing a squeaker
at the beetle and saw everything—the beetle, dear, the

detective, you know, yes, I just wanted to make *that* clear before you say any more, well, then the toads took our names and addresses, but you don't suppose I gave them *your* address, really, darling, you don't trust me at all, I just said, " Megan Lloyd George, Wales," and after that I had the man crawling, positively *genuflected*, so you needn't worry about *that*, need you, darling, I mean, *whenever* I have the smallest trouble with the police I always tell everyone " Father's a judge of the High Court, and you *must* keep his name out of the papers," so that was all right.'

' Well, that was really all—only of course Toots was rather tiresome—Toots, darling, Toots Fortescue, because he would insist on being arrested, and it took the whole of Scotland Yard to prevent him, a great pity he wasn't arrested, I thought, because he totally *devastated* the rest of the night, well you see, after that we were so utterly *saturated* with everything that we simply had to take an airing in Tommy's bus, and of course Toots *would* bring all the balloons and all the streamers and simply snowed them over Fleet Street at about sixty miles an hour, which was too much on a Sunday morning, as I told Tommy—wasn't I right, darling ?—so I dare say if you were to go down Fleet Street now, you'd find the *Daily Telegraph* simply *inundated* with balloons and streamers, and Hermione sang " Brown Girl, I love you " all the way up Ludgate Hill, well, that sort of thing takes all the pleasure out of a party, don't you think, Dad, though I must say St. Paul's looks utterly *captivating* when there are no foul City men about, not that I got much pleasure out of the party, I shouldn't have gone only I took a bad knock—yesterday—a knock, darling—perhaps you don't know about that, no, I haven't told any one, well, Harry Freemantle has picked another doe—he's clicked elsewhere, he's connected, O Lord, darling, he's engaged, he's plighted—now do you get me ? No, it's all right, Dad, there's nothing in it, my own fault, I expect, but still I *had* sort of, well, expectations, so to speak, silly of me, I'm not squealing, but you do see, don't you, how I simply had to go out and detonate somewhere after all, if only to show I didn't care two hoots, and, after all, it's much better than exploding in the home, isn't it, darling ? '

' So you see, darling, that's why I got Tommy to throw a party, and there you are, Tommy's a lamb, don't think I'm blaming you, Dad, but perhaps, if you'd known that, you wouldn't have dragged me up here and lectured me on a Sunday morning, I'm late for church as it is, and I've nothing for the plate, have you a sixpence, darling, I never have a sou, and that reminds me—everybody agrees that my allowance is absolutely *penurious*, darling, I dare say you've noticed I haven't a *fragment* of anything to wear, and what I have got is *centuries* old, all my hats ought to be in a mausoleum, really, darling, I might be a spinster or married or something, don't think I mind for myself, Dad, I'd just as soon go about like A Present from Surbiton, but it's you I'm thinking of. I do hate not doing you credit, see, darling, you being a Judge and all that, and of course, if I hadn't looked like the very first Ford, perhaps Harry Freemantle— no, never mind that, but if you *could* manage the *flimsiest* little extra, say another fifty pounds, darling— Well, that's too flower-like of you, Dad, there's a kiss for you, and perhaps a tiny cheque on account do you think, Dad you're an archangel, there's another, well, now you're not to say another word or I know I shall miss some simply *pulverizing* sermon, good-bye, darling, be good, oh, you'll have the cheque ready, won't you, because if it's at all possible we've promised to bail Toots out some time to-day, O gosh, I forgot to tell you Toots *was* arrested after all, you're not shocked, are you, darling, because deep down we've all got hearts of precious gold, and as for me, I'm a perfect pansy of a girl ! Ta-ta ! '

I

THE MASCOT

'WHY shouldn't one run down to Brighton?' said George Rowland casually, one Saturday morning.

'Why should one?' I answered.

'Why *does* one?' said George darkly.

'I don't know,' I said. '*Does* one?'

'One does,' said George, 'but two are better. If you want to see life, old boy, you come to Brighton.'

. . . . .

If you want to see death, old fellow, you go to Brighton in George's new car. It is a monster, and the latest thing in monsters; it has a bonnet the length of an ordinary two-seater, and within the bonnet are concentrated the strength and swiftness of an hundred horses; it has tyres a foot thick and wheels like the shield of Achilles.

Before the front seats are placed nine impressive -ometers or gauges, with jiggling needles, by which the driver may know his speed per hour, the time of the day, the temperature, the oil-pressure, the petrol-pressure, the amount of water in the carburettor, the condition of the magneto and many other things. There is nothing to show the day of the month or the state of the tide.

The bonnet is of shining aluminium, and on the foremost extremity or prow there stands a naked female figure in silver, in the attitude of a bad swimmer about to dive into the sea on a very cold day.

The speedometer, I noted, was marked up to a mere hundred miles per hour.

I was parked in the front seat, and we shot out of the garage, roaring like lions.

' Isn't she a darling ? ' said George, as we reeled round a refuge. ' What shall I call her ? '

' I should call her " The Wise Virgin," ' I shouted, with a frightened glance at the speedometer.

' Why ? ' he shouted back, whizzing past a steam-roller.

' Because she's just going to throw herself out of the car.'

' I'm talking about the *car*.'

' I'm talking about the Naked Nymph,' I yelled, holding on my hat, ' the Silver Suicide.'

' Oh,' said George, ' she's Bellona,' and added strangely : ' The Goddess of Speed, you know.'

' No, George, I didn't know that. Am I to be the human sacrifice ? '

' She's my mascot,' said George.   ' Brings me luck.'

' A painless death, I suppose ? '

George knows my views of his driving well enough, but at the beginning of a journey I generally try to rub them in.   It is no use.

' Whenever I've hit anything with her on board,' he said with satisfaction, ' the other fellow's had to pay.'

' That's very comforting,' I murmured, and we shot into the country, passing every car in sight. Half of them, I noticed curiously, had naked silver ladies like our own, about to fling themselves in front of the wheels ; on the other half were silver angels, pointing meaningly to heaven.

'What happens, George,' I shouted, 'if you hit a car with the same mascot as your own ? '

'Never do, old boy,' said he.

'You nearly did then,' I said with outward calm.

'Damned fool can't drive,' growled George.

'It's funny,' I said at the top of my voice, 'I have been near to extinction in a motor-car many times, but in no case that I remember was the car which carried me at fault.'

'Sorry, old man, I didn't catch.'

I gave it up. The monster roared ahead, eating up the miles ; and I now understood why so many people walk to Brighton. Trees, churches, villages rushed at the car and vanished with a whizz behind. In vain for us the Spring had decked the boughs, in vain the primrose lurked below the hedge. At fifty miles an hour a dandelion is just as sweet. In vain, at the cross-roads, dimly seen, the Automobile Association scouts punctiliously saluted us. My nose was cold, my feet were warm, my eyes were watering ; strapped under a great rug I could not find my handkerchief. How I love a spin in a good car !

George crouched happy over his wheel, one eye on the speedometer and one foot in the grave.

'Fifty-five,' he grunted as we neared a town. 'Afraid I shan't get seventy out of her to-day. Not on this road.'

'Sickening ! ' I shouted.

George threw me a quick glance and slowed down.

'Sorry, old man,' he said, 'I forgot. You're nervy, aren't you ? '

' I wasn't,' I said : ' I dare say I shall be.'

' Brighton'll do you good, old man. There's a whole crowd of nervy people there.'

' If they went there by car,' I began, ' I don't won——' But George had jammed his foot on the accelerator again.

We passed at a decent pace through the town and I breathed again. The blood returned to my cheeks ; I got at my handkerchief and wiped my eyes, and, looking about me, I enjoyed the sight of my fellow-creatures moving happily about on foot. For the first time I wished there were more towns in the country.

Once through the town, George let out the cut-through—a technical term ; there was a sound like the snarl of a leopard about to eat a dog and the country-side began to flicker like a Cubust film again. The Silver Suicide danced like a mad thing. Forty ! Forty-five ! Fifty ! At fifty-five I prayed. At fifty-seven we crossed a sudden little rise over a tiny bridge. The car left the ground, I swear, and I shot into the air. Descending, I found myself, with some surprise still in the front portion of the car. ' Sixty ! ' said George with pride, slowing down. ' How's that, old man ? '

' Very nearly out,' I said ; and then with a sudden inspiration : ' I say, George, do you think we could stop and have a drink somewhere ? I've a hideous thirst.'

' Right,' said George. ' So have I.'

' Eaten too many miles, I expect,' I said feebly.

At the next ' Lord Nelson,' we stopped. I lingered outside a moment, admiring the car. When we started again the Brighton Road was one long procession of cars, and we began the frightening routine of treading on their heels, barking at them, squeezing past them and turning in our seats to glower at the occupants. After about four miles of this I said suddenly: ' Hullo ! she's gone.'

' Who's gone ? '

' The Silver Suicide.'

' Good Lord ! ' said George.   ' So she has.   Shaken off.   That's funny.'

' I expect it was at that little bridge,' I said.   ' I nearly disembarked myself.'

' No good going back, I suppose,' said George sadly.

' Not a bit,' I said decidedly.   ' You'd better ask the A.A. men on our way back.'

' Well, well,' sighed George.   ' I wouldn't lose that mascot for the world.   I shouldn't wonder if we had a smash now,' he added gloomily.

' It would be awful if you had to pay,' I murmured.

The rest of the drive I thoroughly enjoyed.   The change in George's style of driving was remarkable. He seemed to have lost his nerve.   On the other hand he had recovered his caution.   We ambled along at a respectable twenty-five or thirty, slowing down at all curves and hooting at corners in a manner that was almost cowardly.   We were now constantly passed by other cars, whose drivers turned and glowered at us for obstructing them, while George glowered at them for reckless driving.

But the change, of course, had nothing to do with the Silver Suicide.

' Afraid this is a bit of a crawl, old man,' he said very soon ; ' fact is, from now on the road is one long

police-trap—and I'm not taking any risks of that
kind.'

'Quite right, old fellow,' I said. I admired the
young leaves upon the trees ; I decided that I would
bow to the A.A. men but not smile ; and I had time
to marvel at the numbers of those who, like ourselves,
were southward bound for Brighton. It was a wonder,
that endless stream of pilgrims, muffled figures, so
much alike, and all protected by Nymphs and Angels
from the perils of the road. They looked neither to
the right nor to the left, but kept their eyes fixed upon
the South, as persons conscious of a quest. And as they
flashed ahead of us, one after another, there mounted
in me the sense of a common urgency and purpose,
and I wondered ' What do they seek in the City of
Dreams ? '

I asked George.

George assumed the tone and air of a man who knows
the world.

' You wait,' he said.

And so we came to Brighton, unscathed. And at
Brighton I posted the Silver Suicide to the A.A.
representative at Croydon, where on the Monday we
retrieved her.

' George,' I said as we went in to lunch, ' if I were
you I should call your mascot " True Love ".'

' Why, old man ? '

' Because absence only makes her stronger.'

' Don't follow, old chap,' said George.

II

THE WICKED PIER

THE richer Romans, if I remember right, were fond of thrusting little piers into the sea in front of their holiday villas at Baiæ, Capri and elsewhere. At about the same time the morals of the Emperors took a turn for the worse and the Roman Empire decayed.

There are those who might draw a sinister comparison when they see for the first time the monstrous pleasure-piers of Brighton thrust out so arrogantly into the pure stream of Ocean. But George and I were not among them. Indeed, the piers of Brighton are her glory. It is the sea which is the blot. Who would suppose that that grey and dingy fluid which lops about the West Pier is the same that washes the shores of Cornwall and Palermo, and is described by many poets as blue ? It is not necessary, however, to look at the sea. There are corners in the band-house where a man may sit with his face towards the town and think himself in Camberwell again.

Except, of course, for the moral tone. George insisted that we should spend our first afternoon on the pier for the sake of the moral tone. He called it ' doing the penny-in-the-slot machines '; but I gathered that the penny-in-the-slots were somehow mysteriously connected with the moral tone.

At the end of the pier there is a vast quadrangular theatre, hung like a fairy mushroom o'er the sea. About it there blew without ceasing a frightful east wind, and I longed for the genial frowst of Kensington. But the whole of Kensington has not so many penny-in-the-slots as are set about this theatre. We changed all our money into coppers and thoroughly enjoyed ourselves for about an hour. In theory the penny-in-the-slots are provided for the young; in practice, however, few modern children have either the money or the leisure for a real slot-orgy such as George and I indulged in. A number of children followed us about and extracted wistfully a vicarious pleasure from our excesses.

My favourites are those machines by which my money is returned. And I turned with joy to my old friend the 'Guess-Your-Weight' machine. Once more I guessed my weight to a pound, and heard once more the golden clatter of the returning penny and knew that I had won. Is there a sound on earth more exquisite than this? Here is the one sensation that never stales. It is the one moment when I feel that I am greater than a machine; that Man is important; that I am an important man and capable of greatness. After all, I have pitted my wits against a Robot, staked all upon my brains, and here is my capital returned to me intact. Practically, it is making money. To put in a penny and receive a penny in exchange—many are the financiers, after all, who would be glad if they had done as much at the ending of the day.

I pocketed my penny and studied once more the lists printed over the dial, showing the average weight of healthy men, women and children of various heights. And I turned away, as usual, with a certain sense of humiliation, for weight is not my strong point, and I find that I work out at a woman of five feet seven.

However, the next few slots restored my pride; for I

won heavily. The most delicious machine of all is that which has a little ship floating in real water, and when the penny is inserted the ship is released, and, drawn by some invisible but irresistible magnet, begins to move stealthily across the water to destruction—an awful thing to see. But by frantically turning a nautical little wheel outside it is possible to steer the ship through bridges of inconceivable narrowness into a safe harbour, when the penny is returned. I reckon that in my time I have made a substantial sum of money out of these machines. I seldom fail to save that little ship. It calls up qualities in a man which every man *knows* that he possesses, but never in real life has any chance to display—coolness, quickness, nautical aptitude, and a clear notion of the distinction between right and left. I made sevenpence out of the ship. George, I was happy to see, invariably steered the ship to ruin.

Time after time my penny clattered back. I do not as a rule invest much capital in the 'Test Your Strength' machines; but to encourage George, who was growing a little moody, I took him on at the Grip-Gauge, with disastrous results. The strongest possible grip is 600, and the average grips of different trades and professions are noted above the machine :

Farmers .	.	.	.	.	.	. 470
Bankers	.	.	.	.	.	. 300
Lawyers .	.	.	.	.	.	. 325
Boilermakers	.	.	.	.	.	. 430
Moulders	.	.	.	.	.	. 470
Paperhangers .	.	.	.	.	.	. 325
Stenographers .	.	.	.	.	.	. 300

Travelling Men	.	.	.	.	400
Telegraphers	.	.	.	.	290
Dentists .	.	.	.	.	360

and so on.

George gripped first, grew very red in the face, and registered 400, the grip of a Travelling Man. I then seized the handle, and—to this day I know not why— the needle shot round the dial, past Paperhangers and Boilermakers, past Plumbers and Moulders, and rested at 595. I was the strongest man in the world.

George said I had not gripped fair. I *gave* him a penny, and told him to grip as I had. He went red in the face again and reached 285—a little lower than the Telegraphers.

I cannot think of anything that I have enjoyed so much.

When I had made about five shillings George took me into a small room called ' Joyland.' It was entirely full of penny-in-the-slot machines, but of a different character. They were like large cameras, with little windows of glass, through which the pleasure-seeker was invited to look. Over them were written such legends as ' The Lifeograph—Montmartre—And Very Nice Too '—' What the Butler Saw '—' The Harem Girls at Play '—' Why Mary Blew Out the Light '— and ' What Tommy Saw in Paris (for adults only).' One or two were even marked with the awful warning —' For Men Only.'

A young adult left the last-named machine as we entered and slunk away, not meeting our eyes.

One felt that yet another Brighton boy had stood face to face with Sin.

' Come on,' said George. ' We'd better see the whole of Brighton while we're about it.'

George took ' The Harem Girls at Play ' and I took ' What Tommy Saw in Paris.'

I put in a penny and peered into the secret box. There was a clatter and a great light shone within. . . .

If one is going to be wicked it is as well to be wicked in an old-fashioned style. Tommy went to Paris, I judged, in about the year 1890. And what he saw there was an exceedingly Victorian young lady of English and suburban birth, holding a bicycle more up-to-date than herself. One foot was on the pedal, and, clothed in an open-work black silk stocking, one saw her ankle immodestly exposed. Her hat was large and circular and plentifully adorned with feathers. Her hair was arranged in the style of long ago—a ' bun ' behind and a kind of wedding-cake before.

This vision passed with a click, too soon, too soon. It was succeeded by the same young lady sitting in an apple-tree and dangling from a bough a single foot, on which was no shoe but only a stocking. Next I saw her lying well wrapped up upon a stony beach (doubtless one of the shores of the Seine), and at a little distance a man with a very large moustache and an open umbrella. Again, sitting upon a stool, with one foot quite naked in a hip-bath. Again, in walking-dress, but upside-down. Again, fondling a cat and wearing an expression of innocence which nothing in the picture belied. Again, sitting in a boat and in a daring Victorian blouse, the hair falling about her ample shoulders. The other pictures I forget.

I know not what Tommy did when he saw these shocking sights, but I am afraid I laughed aloud.

I then went and had a peep at George's Harem Girls,
who were, it seemed, three daughters of Norwood,
pillow-fighting on a staircase in the day-costume of 1870.
We laughed so much that a man came in and looked
at What the Butler Saw. This machine, however,
was apparently broken. And when the man had kicked
it and shaken it for some time he looked angrily at
us and went out, using bad words. For if it is rapture
to put in a penny and receive a penny back, to put
in a penny and receive nothing at all is the blackest
misery.

We walked back to the Cosmopole, passing on our
way a cluster of respectable old ladies and gentlemen
huddled round the band-house. I thought again of
all that legend of pleasure and wickedness which hangs
over Brighton, of all those muffled hurrying motorists
who passed us on the Brighton Road. Where were
they ?

' George,' I said, ' this is all very well ; but what
does Tommy see at *Brighton* ? '

' You wait,' said George darkly.

III

THE CHILDREN'S HOUR

WE were in the American Bar. George and a hearty
man had fallen into conversation, and we all sat
down at one of the tables. The hearty man, who
was robust and florid, was the only person I met
in Brighton who never once spoke about bronchitis
or the bitter wind. He was the kind of man whom
I envy above all others, the man I sometimes wish

that I could be. He was possessed, it was evident, of extreme wealth. He wore a pearl tie-pin. He wore a check suit. He knew the world. He understood about ' odds ' and ' doubles ' and ' naps ' and things. He had travelled. What part he played in the daily labour of our sphere I cannot guess, but it must have been a big one. And he knew ' good ' stories.

Heavens ! the good stories that man had in his head ! Whatever George said, whatever object at the moment caught his eye, a glass, a table, a match-box, a nose, it reminded him of a good story. For myself, I must have heard a million good stories in my time. Every time I hear a good story I say to myself : ' I must remember that.' And two days later I have forgotten the very theme of it. Or, if not, I retain only a few disconnected fragments, frequently indelicate, which, being put together, are neither interesting nor funny. Yet other men, whose intellects I despise, remember every good story they hear, atmosphere, dialogue, point and all. Their minds are a storehouse of good stories. Mine is a sort of filter.

The hearty man's best stories were without exception indelicate, though not extremely so. They cannot be printed here. Indeed, I have forgotten them. But he gave them verisimilitude by the cunning way in which he introduced them. He would throw off a preamble or parenthesis or two, explaining that at the period in question he chanced to be in Hong Kong, Alaska or the Malay States ; and one generally felt that the thing had happened to *him*. Incidentally too he would mention the large sums of money which he had amassed or sacrificed at the time in Hong

Kong, Alaska or the Malay States. ' I dropped five thousand that trip ' was one of his favourite asides. ' I cleared a hundred thousand dollars ' was another. On the whole, by a little rapid arithmetic, I calculated that, after a lifetime of financial adventure, the man was now ' all square.'

He was admirably genial, and George and he were firm friends by about half-way through the second cocktail. George knows good stories too, and gave him story for story. I listened humbly and in silence, except when I said dutifully : ' Ha ! that's a good one ' ; or when the hearty man said : ' Have you heard the story about the man in New York ? ' and I said : ' No.' I wondered sometimes what would happen if I said ' Yes.' For in fact I have heard all the stories about the man in New York.

I am no longer surprised at anything that may happen to the man in New York. He leads a life of adventure, devilry and repartee which seems as natural now as the barbarities of the ancient classical legends. What did surprise me was the new light that was thrown by the conversation on George's past history and present circumstances. As I listened I realized with astonishment that George in his short life had knocked about the world at least as much as the hearty man. It was entirely new to me, for example, that George had taken part in a Revolution in Mexico, and had held a high post under General HUERTA. Nor did I previously know that he had once bought two hotels at Melbourne and gambled them away the same night at poker.

And I noticed that, although between them the two men must have traversed most of the habitable globe, the places which they had *both* visited were very few. ' Ever been to Alex. ? ' George would begin. The hearty man had never been to Alexandria, and the story continued. ' I remember one night in the Club at Alex.——' But once, when it looked as if George was going to remember one night at Singapore and it turned out that the hearty man had been in a street-fight at Singapore, George told him about a night at Sydney instead. (It seemed to be understood between them that Australia was George's, and most of America. The other man specialized in the East, with Russia and South Africa thrown in.)

The hearty man ordered a third round of drinks, and George went from strength to strength.

' When I went *back* to Mexico,' he said, ' it was a very different story.'

' What year was that, George?' I asked thoughtlessly.

' Nineteen-nineteen, old boy,' George answered easily. ' Sailed in February. In a tramp,' he added.

' I didn't know you were demobilized then, old man,' I said.

' I wasn't,' said he, looking me in the eyes. ' They seconded me.'

' " Seconded," eh ? ' said the hearty man. ' Secret Service ? '

' Something like it,' George admitted modestly.

' Secret Service, George ? ' I echoed, staggered, I must confess.

' Yes, old boy.'

' You never told me about it,' I said.

' One doesn't, you know,' said George mysteriously. ' Not at the time.' And he went on to tell us how he had held the Plaza at Iquique with one machine-gun and a dozen loyal *ponchos*—' peasants, you know.'

I began to feel very humble and naked, sitting there silent with no story to tell. The conversation of the group on my right sounded more congenial and I listened to them for a little. There were four of them, and the two ladies were principally adorned with black velvet, diamonds and jet.

' I didn't see you on the pier to-day, Mr. Wiggs,' said one of the men mournfully.

' Wind's too cold,' said the other. ' There's a lot of this bronchitis about.'

' It's a bitter wind, you're right,' said a lady's voice.

' Fresh air never did a man harm,' said the first man, who evidently enjoyed robust health.

' Fresh air does more harm than ever it does good, *I* say.'

' It depends how you are in yourself. If you're well *in* yourself, there's nothing hurts you. And if you aren't there's nothing like a hot whisky and lemon.'

' What I say is if you're going to get bronchitis you'll *get* bronchitis, and no amount of stopping indoors won't save you.'

' You've hit it, Mrs. Farrell. My husband always said the same.'

' Your husband had a strong constitution, I dare say. Some of us can't *stand* an east wind.'

' It's all according to what you're accustomed to, it's true. My husband lived a very open-air life, of *course*. And he never had a day's sickness, not till the day he was drowned.'

Then followed in a firm voice what I believe to be

a password at Brighton, for I had heard it twice already that evening.

'Well, all I can say is, you won't find *me* on the pier with all this bronchitis about.'

'Talking of bronchitis,' said the second man, lowering his voice, ' you know the old story about the Welsh doctor ? '

' No, Mr. Farrell.'

' Well, if the ladies will forgive me——? ' said Mr. Farrell doubtfully.

' Mrs. Meadows don't mind *what* she hears,' said Mrs. Farrell comfortably.

' Speak for yourself, Mrs. Farrell, please.'

' I'm speaking for *you*, my dear.'

' Go on, Mr. Farrell.'

Mr. Farrell looked about him and lowered his voice still lower.

I turned away, humiliated again. Everybody at Brighton, it seemed, knew a story except myself. I felt that I could not sit silent there much longer in that hour of stories, that haunt of story-tellers. I racked my brains. Long ago, I recalled, I had known a story. It had something to do with an artist's model ; but that was all I could remember about it. Then there was one about three American regiments. Some one said to somebody else. . . . And I fanced the man in New York came into it somehow. But it had gone.

Could I not invent one ? I tried. ' A man in New York went to a doctor. . . .' ' An artist's model was walking down Cheapside. . . .' ' The Mayor of Brighton was bathing at Alexandria. . . .' It was no good. I have always despised this kind of story as an easy

second-hand way of winning applause. And I realized
with shame that I could not even *invent* one.

Meanwhile George and the hearty man were up to
the neck in reminiscences. The hearty man had just
described a tiger-hunt he had witnessed. He himself,
it seemed, had slain a man-eater with his own hands.
As for George, he had become a brand-new person.
I heard without surprise that he had been a mining
engineer. He had come to London with half a crown
in his pocket. He had bought oil-shares on the
ground-floor and sold in the nick of time at 120, though
unhappily the fortune thus amassed he had staked,
and lost, at Monte Carlo on a single throw. And at
the present moment he was financing a big theatrical
show in London and had come down to Brighton to
look for a Beauty Chorus.

At this piece of information the hearty man could
scarcely conceal his respect and admiration, and he
ordered another round of cocktails. He then explained
to George that he had to leave early the following
morning as Scotland Yard had asked for his assistance
in the investigation of a murder.

In the pause that followed I determined to strike
a blow myself.

'Well, sir,' I said, 'I'm sorry you won't be here
to-morrow, because I'm afraid you'll miss a lot of fun.'

'How's that, sir?' said the man, as if he had seen
me for the first time.

I looked George in the eyes. 'I've invented a
Death Ray,' I said simply. 'I've come down here
to make a few experiments.'

IV

THE SURPLUS MALE

DINNER was over. We had now passed some seven hours in Brighton, and I had not yet discovered the particular lure of Brighton. Most of the time had been spent at the Cosmopole, and I now felt that we should make some contact with the less opulent society of the town.

The man behind the American Bar had told us that there was a great deal of life at the People's Dreamland. And with this authority I persuaded George to pay it a visit.

But he insisted on changing back into ordinary clothes.

The People's Dreamland is just another Palais de Danse, but a very fine and extensive one. A vast place, the size of a London church. It was full of smoke, Chinese lanterns and the syncopated cooing of two bands. When one band stopped the other band began. The floor was thick with the moving figures of the People.

A throng as numerous as the dancers stood or sat behind the stout barriers which guard the floor, watching the dancing. We stood and watched the watchers. They were about equally divided between the male and the female. And a careful study of the scene revealed the fact that it was tragic. For it was evident that the ladies who were not dancing were not dancing because they had not been asked to dance.

Much is written about the surplus woman; but too little is said about the surplus male. It was equally

evident that the men who were not dancing were not
dancing because they had nobody to dance with.   One
of these I saw timidly introduce himself to a surplus
lady, and with her take the floor.   The self-introduc-
tion was clearly permitted by local etiquette.   And
why, I wondered, do not all the surplus men pair
off with all the surplus ladies ?   At that moment I
had my answer.   A very unattractive surplus man
approached a very plain surplus woman, bowed
gallantly and said something.   A moment later he
walked away again, looking crushed, self-conscious
and a little red.   The plain surplus woman thought
nothing of him.   But she had no further offers.   The
other surplus men thought nothing of her.   Instead
they vainly cast their eyes on the charmers revolving
in the arms of other men.   Did I not say it was a
tragic scene ?

EUCLID, in one of his easy generalizations, remarked
that things which are equal to the same thing are equal
to one another.   It may or may not be so.   But a
sadder and profounder truth is this—that people who
are surplus to the same people are also surplus to one
another.

The band played ' The Wooden Soldiers.'   The
blood rushed to my feet.   But we—we too were
surplus.   However, we stood near the pen marked :

DANCING PARTNERS—6d.

and I called George's attention to this.

George threw a brief and disparaging glance over
the ladies in the pen and made an ungallant observation
which I will not repeat.   George, like the other surplus
men, has a very high standard.

' I think I shall take a walk round, old boy,' he said, ' and see if I can see anything.'

' All right, old man,' I said. ' I shall have sixpennyworth.'

' Huh ! ' said George, with another glance at the unfortunate D.P.s. ' Bet you a bob you don't.'

' Done,' I said. ' That will pay for a couple.'

George strolled away.

I stood a short time trying to decide which of the D.P.s had the most culture.   And while I stood there a young lady came towards me, smiling slightly as if she knew me.   I smiled back slightly, thinking that perhaps she did.   When a few feet off she peered up into my face (there was a lamp just behind me), and suddenly her own face seemed to freeze ; she turned away and disappeared into the crowd.   Evidently we had never met.

While I was still wondering at this strange event, another young lady approached and did exactly the same thing, except that she smiled much less and froze considerably more.

I looked about me, wondering.   I looked above me and behind me.   Behind me I saw a little alcove with some empty chairs.   Above me I saw :

DANCING PARTNERS—6d.

It was my turn to freeze.   *I had been taken for a Sixpenny Dip !*

I did not resent that so much.   I have no false pride.   What did rankle was the suspicion that two different surplus daughters of Brighton had come to the conclusion that I was not worth sixpence.

I decided to change my position.

But at that moment a third young lady approached, a lady infinitely more pleasing than the others. Indeed, she was quite definitely pleasing by any standard.

In her hand was a pink ticket, which she held out to me with a shy but charming gesture. I took it, of course. On it was printed :

PEOPLE'S DREAMLAND.
ONE DANCING PARTNER
SIXPENCE.
NO GRATUITIES.

I say ' of course.' My pride was soothed ; my heart was touched. I warmed to the girl. After all it is not every man who can say that a strange, charming, respectable young woman has deliberately paid money to dance with him—has, as it were, *singled him out* for honour. We took the floor.

I remembered with some concern that in theory a dancing partner is generally an instructor, and was relieved to find she was not likely to want a lesson. She danced beautifully.

' Been on this job long ? ' she said kindly, putting me at my ease.

' Not long,' I said uncomfortably. I decided that very shortly I would tell her the truth.

' Takes it out of you, I dare say,' she said, ' so much of it. What I mean—well, every day 's a *lot*, isn't it ? '

' Some days are better than others,' I said.

' Well, it 's all according, isn't it ? An' I dare say they don't give you any too much, if the truth was known ? '

It struck me that I was being cross-examined.

' I can't complain,' I said.

'That's one way of looking at it, of *course*,' she said. 'I wonder you don't get a job at the Cosmopole. A boy I knew was taken on as a Professor.'

I decided that it was becoming very difficult to tell her the truth.

'Quite a crowd to-night,' she went on.

'We're generally busy Saturdays,' I answered. (This style of conversation is very easily acquired.)

'Yes, there's a lot of people here.'

'Do you come here often?'

'Not what you might call often. I like a bit of pleasure now and then, it's true. But my friend doesn't dance, and I don't care to dance with every one myself.'

'Every one?' I echoed wonderingly.

'A lot of girls here,' she said severely, 'will dance with the first thing that asks them—intro or no. Well, it's all according to taste, but I don't dance without an intro myself—not if it was the Prince of Wales.'

I decided that it was quite impossible to tell her the truth now.

'Can you do the Heeby-Jeebies?' she said suddenly.

'Of course,' I murmured. I could as soon do the Sword Dance.

'Show me,' she whispered. She had a charming whisper.

'The fact is——' I began. 'The fact is——' I continued, wondering desperately what the fact was; and then I had an inspiration. 'I have to charge extra for a lesson.'

'Oh, dear,' she cooed. 'How much?'

'A guinea,' I said boldly.

'It's a lot of money, isn't it?' she sighed. 'I

mean to say—a *guinea*—well, it *is* a lot, isn't it ?   For
one lesson, I mean.'

' It is,' I said earnestly.   ' It isn't worth it.'

' Oh, well,' she said sensibly, ' what's worth it and
what you want's two different things, isn't it ?   Hallo,
Loo ! '

She had taken her left hand from my shoulder and
was waving it brightly at a group of people at one of
the tables.   They waved their hands in return and
seemed possessed with some subtle merriment which
they were endeavouring to conceal.   I had an uncomfortable feeling that it had something to do with me.
We danced on.

' Wouldn't my father go on if he saw me now ! '
she said happily, very soon.

' Would he ? ' I said nervously.   I did not like the
implication.

' You'd laugh to see father in one of his rages,' she
chuckled.

' Should I ? ' I wondered.

' Still, it isn't the same thing, is it, not reelly ? '
she said.

' How d'you mean ? ' I said, hopelessly fogged.

' Well, I mean it's not like dancing without an
intro, is it—you being official, so to speak, if you see
what I mean.'

' Of course,' I said.

' Still, it's the first time I've done it, for all that,'
she said, with a sort of satisfied recklessness in her
tone.

My pride, which had been alternately bounding up
and tumbling down during this conversation, now
grandly rose again.   But I was still uncertain and

curious about the motive which had driven this respectable damsel to approach me. Had she, for example, conceived a sudden passion for me, or was I merely a piece of licensed wickedness ?

The music stopped and I led her off the floor.

' What made you do it this time ? ' I asked her boldly.

' Couldn't say, I'm sure,' she said, and blushed a most brilliant blush. ' Oh, well——' she said, embarrassed, ' thanks,' and with a strange smile she left me.

Pushing my way through the throng to my rendezvous with George I had to pass close to her friends' table ; they were all laughing heartily, and I saw my partner, flushed and triumphant-looking.

' Well done, Maud ! ' I heard a man say ; and he handed her half a crown.

' Thanks, Joe,' she said. ' But I don't like to take it. He was ever so sweet. You'd be surprised.'

The truth flashed upon me. *She had done it for a bet.*

The little beast !

. . . . . .

' Ever so sweet.' Oh, well . . .
I lost my bet with George after all.

D

SEEING LIFE (AT LAST)

IN the year 1924 the zealous authorities of our
Metropolis, conscious of the approach of many million
Wemblers from over the seas, began their glorious
campaign to make London clean for the Colonials.
To-day there is scarce a night-club in the town which
can call its soul its own. Let them be never so cunning
and discreet, some gallant constable will climb through
a skylight in the ladies' cloakroom and vindicate the
law at last. That scum, the gay and cultured middle-
classes, are harried ruthlessly from haunt to haunt.
And now, if a man would break the law with impunity,
he must either drink with the nobility at the aristo-
cratic cabaret or bet with the unemployed at public
boxing halls. For only the very rich and the very
poor are safe.

' Small wonder, after all,' I thought, as we entered
the Night-jar, ' that London flocks to Brighton.'
The Night-jar is (or was in 1924, for Heaven knows
if it has survived) the equivalent of Nero's, and my
heart leapt at the sight of it. Here at last was life
and gaiety. Here were half the population of the
Cosmopole—but how changed ! There was the elderly
grey-haired man we had seen at dinner with the
vision in green. Old and feeble he had looked at
dinner, as if every course might be his last ; but now,
erect and sprightly, he stepped it like a two-year-
old. There too were Belle Heather and her handsome
swain, but dancing now as if they enjoyed it. There
too was the hearty man, with a lady almost as

hearty. The band played not delicately, as at the Cosmopole, but wildly, with abandon, and out of time ; and now and then one of the musicians would rise in his place and yell. The scene was positively Continental in its gaiety ; and, so far as I could judge, there was not a policeman present.

George and I sat down at one of the tables and watched. There seemed to be no dancing partners. We were surplus males again.

Presently Mr. Wiggs and his three friends of the American Bar came in, sat down at the next table and began talking about bronchitis, but now with a definitely cheerful note. Mr. Wiggs said something to a waiter and four coffee-cups were brought them. Mr. Wiggs took a sip or two and almost immediately betrayed signs of violent intoxication, like men who drink on the stage. He talked in a loud voice and thumped continually on the table with his fist so that the cups rattled and all the dancers laughed with sympathetic joy. I am nothing if not Bohemian, and, standing up, I peered over Mr. Wiggs's shoulder into his coffee-cup. The liquid in it was golden in colour, and it was bubbly. I judged that it was champagne.

While I was still wondering at this extraordinary thing, Mr. Wiggs rose up shakily and said loudly and petulantly : ' You can say what you like, Mr. Farrell, but this is *my* shout.' He then picked up a plate, dashed it violently on the floor and stood at bay, glaring at Mr. Farrell. The dancers cheered.

To my astonishment the plate did not break. On the contrary, it bounced.

I say, the plate bounced. Not the small bounce of

a strong china plate, but a gay high bounce, as if it were india-rubber.

I picked the plate up.   It *was* india-rubber.

But its upper side was coated with asbestos and painted with the Willow pattern.

' George,' I said, ' this is a very strange place.'

' Quite right, old boy,' said George placidly.   ' I'm going to look for a partner.'

' Don't leave me, old man,' I said nervously ; but he had gone.

Presently he returned with two young ladies.

' This is Miss B-r-r-r-r, old boy,' he said.   ' And this is Miss G-r-r-r-r.   Miss B-r-r-r-r—Mr. Haddock. Mr. Haddock—Miss G-r-r-r-r.'

They were young and childish, lacking in refinement, but very innocent, I judged.   I wondered where George had met them.   I danced with Miss B-r-r-r-r, and while we danced we talked ; but the conversation soon languished, for, whatever I said, she replied: ' You silly man.'   I discovered, however, that her name was Ruby.   But when I danced with Miss G-r-r-r-r, whose name was Pearl, she could only say: ' Clever, aren't you ? ' or ' Think you're clever, I suppose ? '   And to this day I do not know whether I was clever, silly, neither or both.

After the second dance George said he was thirsty and summoned a waiter.   The aged waiter looked at him doubtfully, said ' Very sorry, sir,' and whispered something.   George took out a visiting-card and scribbled something on the back of it.   The waiter took the card away and said something to a large man at the end of the room.   The large man examined us suspiciously and said something to the waiter.

The waiter came back and said: 'Step this way, sir.'
But Ruby said: 'Don't bother, Tom; we'll look
after them.'

Wondering a little, we were led upstairs. Pearl
knocked thrice in a mysterious manner on a door and
we were admitted to a small room, almost bare of
furniture but full of people. All were standing round
a single table, on which were many bottles and a few
glasses.

Ruby said she would like a Port and Lemonade—
the favourite refreshment of the woman of the world,
I am informed. The port for the system and the
lemonade for the soul. Pearl had a Benedictine and
Soda Water, and George in sheer bravado ordered a
Whisky and Gin.

He received this beverage in a cracked tooth-glass.
The whole proceedings had an air of stealth and
scramble such as one would associate with an illegal
picnic. Everything was *wrong*. Those who had liqueurs
drank out of large tumblers and those who had long
drinks had tiny glasses. Some drank out of tea-cups
and others drank from jugs. No one, as a fact, drank
anything very much, but all, like Mr. Wiggs, continued
to imitate the best-known tavern scenes in comic
opera. Indeed, there were not a few who sang.

Carried away, I ordered a double Crême de Menthe.
It was not nice, but it was illegal. It was thrilling. I
had not been so happy since I travelled in America.
We were rebels. We were one with TITUS OATES,
with WAT TYLER, HAMPDEN and the Seven Bishops.
The prices charged were enormous, but George paid
without a tremor. For men will pay anything to break
the law.

Suddenly a bell rang, a whistle was blown, there was a cry of ' Police ! ' Every face was blanched. The utmost excitement and satisfaction prevailed. Every one, it seemed, knew what to do. A sliding panel was drawn back in the wall. The bottles and jugs were whisked away into a secret cupboard, and the glasses, tea-cups, flower-vases, and christening-mugs were emptied into a secret sink. From the same cupboard two Halma-boards and a set of Ludo were produced, and the company, with outward calm, began a number of round games. George and I played ' Snakes and Ladders.'

After a little while the man in charge of the room tiptoed out of the door.

When he returned his face was all smiles. ' False alarm, boys ! ' he cried ; and there were cheers.

But ' What a shame ! ' said Ruby. And that, I felt, was the sense of the House. I have seldom been so disappointed.

' We were in luck, old boy,' said George as we went home. ' It isn't every one they have a raid-night for.'

' What d'you mean ? ' I said.

' All done for your benefit, old boy.'

' Explain, George,' I said huffily.

George explained.

The Night-jar, it seems, began respectably. It had a licence. It has still a licence. It provided good plain dancing partners, with modest uniforms and labelled, in a pen. It provided quiet revelry and modest refreshment. It did not pay. People did not care to take their friends to a place where there was not the smallest chance of a police-raid. Not merely did the butterflies of London cease to come to Brighton, but the young Brightoners took to going to London for the week-end. The proprietors of the Night-jar determined to become disreputable. Every obstacle was put in their way. They begged the magistrates to cancel their licence. The magistrates refused. Desperate, the proprietors put it about that the licence *was* cancelled. The whole place was ' Prohibitionized.' Legal refreshment was invested with all the delicious trappings of illegality and stealth. The label ' Dancing Partners ' was removed. Ruby and Pearl were taken out of their uniforms, dressed in evening dress and became exciting. At reasonable intervals bogus police-raids were provided ; and special raid-nights were arranged ahead for distinguished parties. Meanwhile, men were hired to throw china about and simulate intoxication. The place was now as popular as a sweepstake and the proprietors as wealthy as bookmakers.

' Then where does the real devilry of Brighton go on ? ' I asked.

' You wait,' said George.

I am still waiting.

MORE ABOUT GEORGE

I

BRIGHTER CHEQUES

WHENEVER I see George he duns me for my subscription to ' The Bright Boys,' our dining-club. And not merely for this year's subscription—I could understand that ; he will go on about last year's, a subject which I thought had been decently buried between us. At the monthly dinner last week he caught me in a yielding mood a little after the savoury, but I had no money on me.

' Sorry, old man,' I said regretfully. ' No money on me. Not a bean. I'd pay it willingly, but there you are. I tell you what—I'll pay it next time.'

' I'd take a cheque, old boy,' said George.

' Awfully good of you, old man,' I said. ' I appreciate the compliment, but just this day of all days I haven't brought a cheque-book with me. If I had——'

' Write one on this, old fellow,' said George.

' I beg your pardon, old man ? '

' Write a cheque on this,' he said again.

' But, joy of my heart, I can't write a cheque on the back of a *menu* ! '

' Light of my night,' said George, ' you certainly can. You can write a cheque on anything.'

' Moon of the West, are you jesting ? ' I replied. ' The back of a *menu* at the Gobble-Gobble Restaurant ? It wouldn't be decent.'

' It would be cashed,' said George firmly, thrusting the bill-of-fare before me.

' Would it so ? ' I murmured feebly. ' Well, I've no ink.'

' Here is ink, my soul,' said George. ' Also two pens. Common or quill ? '

' Quill,' I said. I am less legible in quill.

' Now write,' said George.

It is a terrible thing to be given a blank sheet of paper and told to sign away six guineas to another. It also struck me as a little difficult. I had never before considered the literary side of a cheque.

' I don't know what to write, George, old man,' I said. There seemed no harm in making it as difficult as possible.

' *Pay*,' said George, ' is the important word. But you'd better begin with the name of the bank.'

' My bank ? Dash it, old bird, I've forgotten the name of my bank.'

' It's the West London and Yorkshire,' said George.

' Right ; I remember now.' And I wrote :

' *To The West London and Yorkshire Bank, Ltd.,*
    14, *Wink Street, W.*1.

        PAY——'

Naked like that, the word PAY disgusted me. I thought with bitterness of the West London and Yorkshire Bank, Ltd.

' George,' I said, ' are you *quite* sure this cheque will be cashed ? '

' Positive, old boy.'

' Are you, indeed ? ' I thought. ' I wonder.'

I scratched out PAY, wrote PAY again and initialled it, to throw suspicion on the word.   I wrote :

' PAY (*curse you !*) *Mr. George Rowland* (*sink him !*) *or Order, the sum of six guineas—and see he gets no more.*

£6/6/0.

Yours affectionately
ALBERT HADDOCK.'

' Will they cash that, old man ? ' I said.
' Um,' said George doubtfully.
To remove all doubt I added a little pencil sketch of George, wearing his pince-nez, by which the meanest banker could not fail to identify him.   I crossed it carefully and wrote the miraculous words ' & Co,' and ' a/c Payee Only.'   I scratched out a word here and

there, wrote it again and initialled it, to throw suspicion
on the whole document. Finally I wrote, 'Not
negotiable,' and prayed that this was true. Then I
added another picture of George in a bowler, in case
he visited the bank like that. The *menu* was a fancy
menu with wobbly edges, and the cheque looked like
the picture above.

'What about the stamp, old man ? ' said George.

' It's about time the club made a gesture,' I replied.
' Either the club provides the stamp for this document
or the whole thing is null and void.'

' I'm not sure it's not that anyhow,' said George
gloomily.

' Null or not,' I answered strongly, ' that's all the
money you get from me.'

I handed him the cheque and I went home flattering
myself that the question of my subscription (or sub-
scriptions) was happily postponed for another month.

Yesterday, however, I crawled into my bank with
the vague idea of extracting money from the monster.
When I say money I mean four pounds. I was positive
I had four pounds in the bank—possibly four and a
half pounds ; I put it no higher than that. I crawled
past the glass cage where Timothy Rugg sits lordly
at his desk and meekly saluted him, as I always do
—though, confound it, Timothy Rugg! Timothy
Rugg was in the Upper Fourth when I was in the
Lower Fifth ! What right then has Timothy Rugg to
lord it in a glass cage while I have to creep in and cash
my overdraft on all-fours ? Timothy Rugg. . . . !

Curse him !

However, I reached the main overdraft counter
and, rising to the perpendicular, peered timidly at

the malignant fellow who looks after the overdrafts from A to L. Judge of my satisfaction and surprise when I observed that the man was positively beaming at me. Doubtless some heavy sum had only to-day been paid into my overdraft—some legacy, some little present from the Government. Recklessly I drew a cheque for twenty pounds, payable to myself alone, a/c payee only, and handed it to the hound across the counter (an evil fellow—I believe he smokes to excess).

'The account is not in funds, you know, Mr. Haddock,' he said, but beaming still, the sly dog. (How difficult it is, I thought, to tell character or state of mind from the expression of a banker!)

'What have you done with that four-pound-ten?' I asked suspiciously.

For answer he produced a grubby document, entirely covered with writing, rubber-stamps and pen-and-ink drawings. It was no other than my cheque to George for six guineas!

'But you don't mean to say you've *honoured* it!' I cried aghast.

'Certainly, Mr. Haddock,' said the creature. 'The account is overdrawn to the extent of one-pound-sixteen.'

'But surely you must see that no sober man could have put his signature to such a document!' I said.

'It has passed through the Bankers' Clearing-House,' he replied. 'We paid it out this morning.'

'But I put " Not negotiable " !' I cried.

'True,' he said. 'It has not been negotiated—in the technical sense.'

'In future,' I said bitterly, 'I shall write " Not cashable—in any sense " ' ; and, turning on my heel, I left the building. It is now clear to me that my bank is capable of anything. Other men, I know, have instituted actions against their banks for wrongfully dishonouring their cheques. What I want to know is —Does an action lie against my bank for honouring a cheque which obviously was never intended to be honoured ? Much as I enjoy the picture of the Bankers' Clearing-House (whatever that may be) painfully poring over the *menu* of the Gobble-Gobble Restaurant and solemnly pronouncing it a sound and valid promissory note, I consider that the Bankers' Clearing-House has evilly entreated me.

For if a man may not evade his creditors by giving them a cheque, then where is Freedom ? Well, they shall pay for it, the bankers ! In future, I swore, I shall write my cheques in verse ; there shall be cross-word cheques and cheques in Esperanto, microscopic cheques on the backs of cigarette-cards, and monstrous cheques the size of posters ; there shall be cheques on scented note-paper and cheques in invisible ink ; they shall be covered with pretty pictures and valuable apophthegms ; the Bankers' Clearing-House shall engage a special staff for the study of my cheques ; they shall labour day and night unravelling my cheques ; and no one of my creditors shall ever refuse a cheque of mine, however mad, for I shall produce the *menu* of the Gobble-Gobble Restaurant, duly rubber-stamped, endorsed and cashed, to be a perpetual example and encouragement !

.   .   .   .   .

The opportunity came soon. This year, as usual, I have had trouble with the Collector of Taxes. And, as usual, the threat of DISTRAINT in red letters has prevailed and I have sent him a cheque.

A female relative on holiday in France has left in my charge a white bulldog of great age, vast intelligence and intermittent ferocity. This creature, Napoleon by name, has never been one of my favourite companions, and I thought that I could well spare him for a day, a week, nay, a month or two. I therefore stencilled on its smooth wide back (an admirable surface) a cheque in the usual prosaic terms for the amount demanded. Napoleon likes to have his back tickled and made approving sounds throughout the proceedings. I attached a twopenny-stamp to his collar and led him by his lead to the Collector's office.

The Collector's menials, as usual, tried to interpose all kinds of bureaucratic obstructions between me and my destination. They wished for the number of my assessment, the reference number of the correspondence, my name, profession, number of children and convictions, colour of eyes and so forth.

I said firmly : ' Take me to the Collector.'

Napoleon is an imitative dog and generally takes his tone from his company. When he caught the firm note in my voice Napoleon growled firmly, and they took me to the Collector at once.

I said to the Collector : ' I am sorry we have had all this bother, but let us now let bygones be bygones. Here is a nice cheque for you. Here is the cheque's licence and two days' rations. Be kind to it, and let it have a raw marrow-bone every second Friday. The cheque is reasonable if well treated, but savage if not. It sleeps in a basket or on the master's bed. Good morning, sir. Good-bye, Napoleon. Rats ! Rats ! Bite 'em, then ! '

Encouraged by my concluding words, Napoleon

approached the Collector, growling deeply, and I departed.

That day, I regret to say, there was a new outburst of telephonery between the Collector and myself. The Collector demanded that I should remove the dog and pay my income-tax. I replied that I had paid or offered to pay my income-tax by cheque, which is *' an order addressed to a banker requesting him to pay to the person therein mentioned or his order the sum of money therein mentioned '* ; that Napoleon was a Bill of Exchange drawn on a banker payable on demand under the Bills of Exchange Act, 1882 ; that, as it happened, I had no cheque-forms left and no paper in the house ; that in these circumstances I had done the one thing possible to meet my obligations promptly ; that if he did not care to demand payment on Napoleon he could do the other thing ; that if he did not take Napoleon to the bank I should take Napoleon to the House of Lords ; that my slogan was ' No Dog— No Income-tax ! '

I think that Napoleon must have recognized my voice on the telephone, for I could hear belligerent noises in the background, and the Collector rang off.

That afternoon the Collector did a cowardly thing. Cowardly yet courageous. He endorsed the cheque to a third party. Like a fool, I had forgotten to make the cheque Not Negotiable. Napoleon loves to have his tummy tickled, but he has never been endorsed by a stranger before, and I don't suppose that he took it too well.

However, he was duly endorsed to a Miss Marion Beige, an actress, who was entitled to a refund. Miss Beige adored Napoleon and the whole transaction, and took the cheque to her bank at once. I am told that she was careful to lead him down the whole of the Strand, where her bank is situated, in the hope of attracting the attention of the Press. What she did attract was the attention of the police, for a large crowd followed her. But Miss Beige, I gather, is one of those instantaneous fascinators who with a single smile can turn steel officialdom into a sentimental pulp. With one glance she satisfied the police that the crowd was not there, and that Napoleon was a promissory note and a normal item in the business of the City. The porter at the bank, where No Dogs Are Admitted, swung open the doors immediately. At the paying-in desk was the usual queue of clients anxious to extract the last penny of their overdrafts before closing-time. Miss Beige walked easily to the head of the queue and, with assistance from a gentleman, handed Napoleon over the counter.

There was some discussion, and one or two people at the head of the queue became almost impatient ; but where you or I would be arrested or sent to a Home the Miss Beiges are often triumphant. The paying-in clerk would gladly have rolled down Ludgate Hill for one soft look from Miss Beige, and now he got a dozen. He was soon persuaded that Napoleon was an ordinary negotiable instrument, and undertook to credit him to Miss Beige's account. (And of course he *is* a negotiable instrument. There can be no argument about it.)

The cheque's behaviour, I hear, was impeccable throughout. It is house-trained and was clean about the bank. It growled once or twice when entered up in the ledger, but more in pride, I gather, than passion, and in general went through the various stages of its career with a kind of dignified content, as if it knew that it was part of the National Revenue.

Where it is now, I am not clear—I believe at the Bankers' Clearing-House ; and I do hope that it is getting its marrow-bone. I warn the authorities there and at my own bank that they had better be careful. Napoleon has his whimsies, and I should not like to be the person who marked him ' R.D.' He might turn nasty. For the rest, I repeat, I am quite prepared to take the legal point to the House of Lords, and I should expect to win. But, if I lost, the apparition of Napoleon confronting the Woolsack at the Bar of the House would be almost worth it.

But there will be no difficulty, I fear. This is the one thing which saddens me, that I do seem to have paid my income-tax.

Next year I shall try George with a heifer.

II

THE HERO

GEORGE's part in this story is discreditable, I allow. And as for Fred Hope's—— !

George and I had been cruising round the narrow ditches and ponds of Norfolk (curiously called ' Broads') in one of the well-known Norfolk sloops (hired for a week), and we were lying up for a night in a certain harbour.

Very early in the morning, which was bright and sunny, I was aroused by strange noises, and shambled

on deck. Just below us was moored a wherry, joined
to the quay by a long landing-plank. A wherry is the
Norfolk equivalent of a barge, a picturesque trader
with a vast brown sail ; but some are fitted with a grand
piano and made all dinky for pleasure parties. And
such was this.

The noise I had heard was the bellowing of a stout
gentleman in the bows, dressed in horn spectacles,
pyjamas and a bowler hat ; and he was bellowing at a
golden-haired lady who was walking down the plank to
the wherry, her skirts held high.

What he said was : ' Hell, Baby, we don't want that-
a-much leg ! '

To which she replied : ' Oh, shucks, you get my
goat ! ' and returned to the quay. Arrived there she
lowered her skirts and tripped down the plank again,
smiling radiantly. That particular harbour is a
picturesque place, even at six o'clock in the morning ;
but neither in the beauty of the scene nor the per-
sonality of the stout man could I see any sufficient
reason for such extraordinary happiness.

The stout man said : ' Aw, Babe, cut out that Sunday
school stuff ! What 's them ankles for ? '

The lady replied with admirable vigour but without
a trace of the buoyant happiness of a few moments
back : ' Now, see here, Mr. Drewitt, if you don't tidy
yer ideas on this leg proposition, I quit. Get me ? '
Then, turning, she walked up the plank, sat down on
a bollard and burst into tears.

To my surprise no one gave any heed to her emotion,
not even the refined and handsome youth whom I
now observed a little further along the quay, dressed
in beautiful white flannels. On the contrary, he poised

himself on the edge as if about to plunge into the water—perhaps by way of protest. Meanwhile a very dark man (no doubt the owner of the flannels) poked his head out of a hatch and regarded the youth with frightful malevolence. Whether the young man would have carried out his chivalrous protest I know not, for at this point the stout man said vigorously : ' Why, Hell, Fred, you gotter look as how you meant it ! '

And the youth, surprisingly in one so refined, replied : ' Aw, cheese it ! I'm through,' lit a cigarette and sauntered off along the quay. The stout man waved his arms heavenward, took off his hat and passionately flung it into the water. And I took a firm hold of our mast to assure myself that I was still in the real world.

Whatever was the nature of these strange proceedings I determined to see them through ; but it was chilly, and I went below for more clothes.

When I returned the lady was again walking the plank, with the old expression of delirious joy. But the only response of the stout man was the remark, tartly delivered : ' Nothing like it, Baby. You gotter tickle up the boys without scarin' the parsons. See ? It's a matter of inches.'

There was now, as the reader may have guessed, a movie-machine-man posted on the quay. And that and something familiar in the features of the handsome Fred, who had returned, suddenly gave me the clue. This must be none other than Fred Hope, the hero of a thousand dare-devil adventures—the man who spent his days leaping from aeroplane to aeroplane, bounding on to express trains, shooting rapids, and being shot out of volcanoes ; probably the bravest man in the entire world. I thrilled.

After some further experiment the exact length of Baby's leg which the public might safely behold was determined, and a new 'shot' went forward. The piece was a 'Dramma,' and it appeared that the dark man was basely luring Baby on to a 'lugger.' Once aboard the lugger and by some folly or negligence of his the wherry would start drifting down into the log-jam at the head of the Colorado rapids, there to be crushed and sunk. But meanwhile Fred Hope would plunge into the raging torrent, battle with tide, rocks, crocodiles and hostile savages, win through to the log-jam, and, jumping from log to log, rescue his bride-to-be on the verge of extinction or dishonour, if not both.

The rehearsal proceeded slowly. For the performers seemed extraordinarily vague about the emotions they were intended to express at given moments, while, to judge from some of her remarks, Baby was even imperfectly acquainted with the details of the plot. Somehow I got the impression that the director was keeping it dark. She stood at the hatch, a pathetic figure, about to descend to danger and dishonour. And she said : ' Say, Mr. Drewitt, do I look cute here, or what-is-it ? '

' Why, I guess you look cute, my dear, with a kind of a mean look in your eyes.'

' Say, there ain't nothing in my contrack about lookin' cute an' mean at the same time.'

Baby's lips trembled dangerously, and the stout man said hastily : ' Oh, well, cut out the mean look, dear heart.'

' Well, I dunno. What am I doin', anyway ? '

' Why, Hell, this guy's got designs on your honour, I guess.'

' How does *he* look ?   I don't want no s'prises sprung on me.'

' Why, he just looks terribly mean.   An' all worked-up an' passionate.   Then you fade out.   See?   And we get Fred looking kind of lonesome in the shack. An' then he comes out on the bank an' does his leap to destruction.   Say, Fred, you gotter look a bit more careless on that ; like death don't mean nothing to you in the circs.   See ? '

' Aw, well, get on with it.'

I have often wondered whether these heroic stars actually perform the desperate deeds attributed to them, or whether at the critical moments their places are taken by dummies, or the unemployed, or what. And I was delighted to think that I should now discover. But, alas, I am still wondering.   For presently a hired waterman poked his head out and said something about breakfast.   And Mr. Drewitt said : ' Why, that's a notion.   We'll take the leap to destruction after.'

·   ·   ·   ·   ·

They all disappeared, and I sat and pondered.   I marvelled that one so slim and refined and fair as Fred Hope should be so brave and so resourceful.   And there came into my head a most inexcusable design. I went below and woke up George.

Very soon the hired man appeared and went off into the town.   It was slack water, and this also was favourable to my experiment.   I dropped into our dinghy, rowed stealthily past the wherry and cast off her stern-line—a hateful, piratical act.   Then I returned, unfastened her head-rope and transferred the end to George.   It was my idea to ' bend ' on a considerable

length of spare rope we had and with it make fast
again, so that the wherry would merely drift the length
of the rope.   George however, by accident or malice,
dropped the wherry's line in the water, and, as the
tide had just begun to run out, she sidled slowly
towards the ocean.   And at that I decided to wait
and see the pictures.

The plank fell into the water with a great splash.
The director poked out his head and, with his mouth
full, loudly condemned the situation.   His cast poured
up and ran about the deck, looking singularly worked
up, considering that all they had to do was to catch
hold of the quay with a quanting-pole ; and I expected
at least to see Fred Hope swim to the shore with a
rope in his teeth.   Meanwhile Baby, with shrill cries,
portrayed a series of emotions that would have made
the fortune of any Dramma.

Stricken with compassion at the sight of beauty
in distress (and all through George's fault), I rowed
after the wherry, boarded her and regained the quay
without difficulty (for the tide was still feeble), and
received the thanks of a hero.

You are right.   George was a low hound to do it.
Still, it was interesting.   For what did Fred Hope
do—Fred the shooter of rapids, the resourceful doer
of noble deeds ?

Fred did absolutely nothing.   He just looked terribly
cute.

FAMILY FACES

THE only card-games which it is worth while for a man of sense to waste his time on are those which are not played with cards at all, such as the game which I invented in the smoking-room of the s.s. *Coronado*. It is played with the signed wine-cards which the steward returns to you on the last day of the voyage with the bill. The bills having been paid, two players take their respective packs and deal the cards out one by one, as in ' Beggar my Neighbour.' Whenever the word ' Whisky ' turns up each player cries ' Snap ! ' and the one crying ' Snap ! ' first wins. But a rum punch is joker and takes the pool always.

I played George, and George of course won. I had perhaps more voice, but he had more whisky-cards. And an old gentleman, in bed, sent up from C Deck to ask if the community singing would be continued long, because if so he would like to join us.

' Family Faces ' is just such a game. George and I often go down for the week-end to old Fothergill's. On our last visit we found Mr. Honeybubble there as well. Now Fothergill comes of a very old family and likes to talk about it after dinner. Normally George and I have not the smallest objection to Fothergill's ancestors. We sit snoozing comfortably over Fother-gill's excellent cigars and brandy, while Fothergill climbs happily higher and higher up the family tree. He generally stops at about De Courcy Fothergill, who was a Lord Chief Justice in the reign of Queen Anne. But on this occasion his ascent was frequently and foully interrupted by Honeybubble, who would keep butting in with his own detestable forebears in Lancashire.

Fothergill is not used to this sort of thing, and the atmosphere became uncomfortable and even subsultry. So much so that George and I, roused before our time, began to have fond memories of our own ancestors, and George mentioned his great-uncle, who was first Bishop of Umbobo, until eaten, very properly, by a cannibal. I then spoke of my grandfather the Admiral, and the end of it was that George suggested that when we next met we should all bring photographs or miniatures of our respective families and see which had the best. This meant that Fothergill had to ask Honeybubble for another week-end, which I don't know that he was so terribly keen on; but he did it, and the evening concluded in a lethal hush, like Europe just before the Great War.

Well, we all met again last week-end, and after dinner on Saturday George sent us off to fetch our families. He himself had a packet of photographs the thickness of *Who's Who*.

The game of ' Family Faces ' you have probably played. But you have never played it with George. Don't. George, I think, would cheat at a Charity Spelling Bee. We sat down at the card-table, and George explained the rules of the game, which are that each player plays an ancestor or relation, and the plainest relation pays five shillings, which the handsomest receives. (Well, that is how George explained the rules.) Honeybubble protested that the whole thing was frivolous and not at all what he had expected ; but Fothergill, who has always made a great point of

the fine looks of his ancestors, overruled him, and
the game began.

Fothergill played first ; and he led his ace, the Lord
Chief Justice in the reign of QUEEN ANNE. A fine-
looking old fellow, though perhaps the tiniest bit
dated by his whiskers. I played modestly my Admiral.
Honeybubble with a tremendous air put down Joshua
Honeybubble, J.P., and we all gazed at Joshua.

' That is my great-great-uncle,' he said, ' first
Mayor of Bootle, founded the Bootle Fire Brigade,
fought in the Crimean War, was a friend of RICHARD
COBDEN, Justice of the Peace——'

' But that's no good, old boy,' said George ; ' he
has a face like an onion.'

Now I could not defend this utterance of George's
in a Court of Law, much less a Court of Chivalry. As
a matter of fact the face of Joshua Honeybubble
bore no resemblance whatever to an onion. It was
quite a good face, and I thought myself that it was
a toss-up between Joshua and the Lord Chief Justice
for the best-looker. But the awful thing is that I
do not really care *what* outrage a man does to Honeybubble. So I was silent.

' An *onion* ? ' said Honeybubble indignantly, as if it
would have been pardonable to liken Joshua to a
potato or a mangold-wurzel.

' An onion,' said George—' quite definitely, an onion.'

Honeybubble made an angry sound like the end of
a soda-water bottle.

' It's your turn, George,' I said, to ease the tension,
as it were.

George then played an unmistakable photograph
of Miss GLADYS COOPER.

' That is my mother,' he said simply.

I opened my mouth, astounded (even I, who know George). I realized instantly that both Fothergill and Honeybubble were of that rare kind of bat who would not know Miss GLADYS COOPER if they saw her, and indeed they were both goggling reverently at George's mother. I was just going to speak when George kicked me very viciously on the ankle. It then crossed my mind that, if George was disqualified for a foul, I should very likely have to pay Honeybubble five shillings, and this, I thought, was more than Joshua was worth. So, basely, I confess, I was silent again.

We then voted. George's remark about the onion must have prejudiced us against Joshua, for Joshua had to pay up and George's mother won.

' You to play, Honeybubble,' said George good-humouredly.

Honeybubble then played an ancestor so appalling that I instantly played my good uncle James.

' My aunt Elizabeth,' said Honeybubble. ' A great woman ; she gave all her life to the poor. Married three times, was presented to the QUEEN, Vice-President of the Primrose League—er——'

' But, man,' shrieked George, ' she's in *bloomers* ! '

It was true. She was wearing bloomers and standing beside a bicycle. It was awful.

' I did not understand,' said Honeybubble stiffly, ' that this was to be a Beauty Competition.'

' Well, it is,' said George, and coolly played a rather inferior chorus-girl as she appears in *The Crinoline Girl*.

' My grandmother,' he said, ' on her wedding-day.'

The others loved her, and I bided my time.

The truth is that George had *finessed* too much, for

the rest of us voted for Fothergill's father, a grand-looking fellow. Honeybubble paid, of course.

At this point, by a stupid piece of clumsiness, I knocked George's cards on to the floor. I helped him to pick them up, naturally, and was fortunate enough to secure the top dozen photographs in his pack. I put my ankles well over towards Fothergill and the game proceeded.

Proceeded? It became a procession. In the next round I played George's *fiancée* (for the time being), a lovely girl.

' My step-mother,' I said, ' as a bridesmaid.'

George spluttered but said nothing. I won; Honeybubble lost with an ancestral alderman.

I then played in quick succession Miss TALLULAH BANKHEAD, JUNE, Mr. OWEN NARES, Miss JEAN FORBES-ROBERTSON, LOPOKOVA, Mr. NICHOLAS HANNEN, Miss ANGELA BADDELEY, Captain EDEN, M.P., and the DUCHESS OF YORK. George had brought a wonderful family, but his second eleven were no match for his first. I played one of my own relations now and then to let Fothergill win a trick with his lawyers and big-game hunters and make him happy. Honeybubble continued to play aldermen and bishops and noted philanthropists and aunts and uncles of unimpeachable virtue but unspeakable appearance. He always paid; it was monstrous. After a few tricks even George began to put in a good word for Honeybubble's ancestors, but nothing could save them. I think in the end even Honeybubble voted against them.

And then—I suppose I was tired by the constant strain of invention—I turned up Miss EDNA BEST, and I simply could not think what relation she was.

I had played seven aunts, I knew, and almost as many sisters, but I could *not* remember what other relatives I had exhibited.

'That is my mother,' I said feebly at last. 'Taken at the Boat-race.'

'I beg your pardon?' said Fothergill suspiciously, and George kicked me again.

'You've had one mother already, sir,' said Honey-bubble rather rudely.

'Well, then,' I said, all harassed, 'that is my little daughter.'

And then, of course, there were questions, and then there were explanations, and then there were harsh words, and, what with one thing and another, that week-end was quite difficult. But I do *not* think that Honeybubble will say quite so much about his ancestors in future.

IV

NEGRO COMMERCIALS

I RECKON that the manufacture of negro songs for fashionable audiences must now be a flourishing industry. Almost every day some new specimen of these simple, spontaneous, unaffected and moving little ditties becomes the rage. They increase as rapidly as artificial flowers. Everybody I know has a pet one, and sings it unprovoked in and out of season with a mystical expression and a nasal twang. I do not suggest that the attractive African negroes of Southern North America, busy at their primitive labours in the fields, may not be and have not been inspired to little masterpieces of reflective song. All

I say is that they cannot be inspired *so often*. For one thing the negro does not work so hard. If all the negroes everywhere abandoned their cotton-picking and cane-cutting and rice-growing and shoe-shining and did nothing else but write noble songs for Belgravia, I do not believe that they could produce as many negro songs as I have heard during the last few months.

I may be wrong. But what about that party at the Antons ? All evening the dancing had been gay and indefatigable ; that is to say, about a hundred persons had stood leaning against each other on a shiny floor for fixed periods at regular intervals, while an inaudible band played tunes of which the rhythms were based upon the antics of negroes crossing a swamp and the words described the love-affairs of the same affectionate race. Then there was supper, and after supper the great attraction of the evening— Jem Johnson, the new negro singer, only just discovered by Lady ——. The room was packed. Duchesses were happy to be allowed standing-room, while mere leading ladies and Members of Parliament sat on the floor, crawled under the piano or listened at the key-hole. For everybody had heard that Jem Johnson was too marvellously entrancing.

A fine, upstanding, shy, modest, smiling fellow. And the company thrilled as in his booming bass he announced, *Dere ain't no wimmen in Hebb'n*. The words of the song, which I wrote down hurriedly, were something like this :

> *Dere ain't no wimmen in Hebb'n,*
> *Dere ain't no wimmen in Hebb'n,*
> *An' dis nigger ain't a-goin' to Hebb'n,*
> *'Cos I'm fixed on meetin' my Mammy.*

Yo' Mammy nussed you from a little child,
                    Jem Johnson,
An' you saw Hebb'n when yo' Mammy smiled,
                    Jem Johnson ;
But dere ain't no wimmen in Hebb'n.

> *No, dere ain't no wimmen in Hebb'n,*
> *Dere ain't no wimmen in Hebb'n,*
> *An' dis nigger ain't a-goin' to Hebb'n,*
> *'Cos I'm fixed on meetin' my Mammy.*

I hear de good old preacher say—
                    ' Jem Johnson,
You buy no mo' shoes for Martha Gray,
                    Jem Johnson,
'Cos dere ain't no wimmen in Hebb'n.'

> *Oh, dere ain't no wimmen in Hebb'n,*
> *Dere ain't no wimmen in Hebb'n,*
> *An' dis nigger ain't a-goin' to Hebb'n,*
> *'Cos I'm fixed on meetin' my Mammy.*

As the deep voice trailed away into silence there
was a gasp of ecstasy, and then thunderous applause.
Every one agreed that in all their experience they had
encountered nothing so worthy of remark. One
Duchess fainted. The song indeed was superbly sung,
and I agreed that the effect was *quite* pathetic. As
for the words, there was no doubt that by the end of
the song the poet had definitely made his point.

The next song, a little cameo, was called *Ole Nigger* :

> It's no use niggers t'inkin' dey's white—
> *Play on yo' harp, Ole Nigger !*
> It's no use takin' dem powders at night—
> *Play on yo' harp, Ole Nigger !*
> Put dem fancy petticoats down,
> You got a harp an' I got a crown,
> An', Lord, who'll care if youse black or brown,
> *Playin' on yo' harp, Ole Nigger ?*

You'll never be President of de United States—
  Play on yo' harp, Ole Nigger !
But you'll come first at de Golden Gates—
  Play on yo' harp, Ole Nigger !
Hey, gal, don't you powder yo' face !
What d'you want wid ribbons and lace ?
You'll look fine in de angels' place
  Playin' on yo' harp, Ole Nigger !

The fire and spirit of this song communicated itself to the huddled audience and put them into a frenzy. An intellectual gentleman said that nothing had given him so much pleasure since a particular pose of Polovska's in the Russian Ballet of 1922. On all sides noblewomen of all ages could be seen humming *Ole Nigger*, and doing what they could with a little swaying of the shoulders to strike a negro note. Young Lady —— whispered to me that she yearned for Alabama. An encore was demanded and granted.

The next song, Jem Johnson said, was a little thing sung by the negroes in the cotton-fields, plucking the cotton :

  Don't strike dat butterfly, Nigger,
    He's got wings, like you.
      Dat butterfly
      Am goin' to die
    Same as you an' same as I ;
      But you and I
      Am goin' to fly
    Same as dat dam butterfly ;
  So don't strike dat butterfly, Nigger,
    He's got wings, like you.

  All togeder in de upper air,
  You an' me an' de great Black Bear,
  All good chillun will be flyin' up dere—

Don't strike dat butterfly, Nigger,
He's got wings, like you—
An' it don't matter how you try,
Hidin' in de corners all around de sky,
You'm sure to meet dat butterfly—
Don't strike dat butterfly, Nigger,
He's got wings, like you.

Dat butterfly den he up an' say,
' Hey, you done strike me one fine day,'
An' PETER he take yo' harp away—
So don't strike dat butterfly, Nigger,
He's got wings, like you-oo,
Dat butterfly
Am goin' to die
Same as you an' same as I,
An' you an' I
Am goin' to fly
Same as dat dam butterfly ;
So don't strike dat butterfly, Nigger,
He's got wings, like you-oo.

No one had heard any of Jem Johnson's songs before. All marvelled at their freshness, but agreed that
they had the traditional simplicity and feeling—little
thoughts cleverly captured and perfectly exhibited.
Lady —— said they reminded her of some exquisite
bloom set by itself in a Venetian vase, or a flawless
jewel reposing on a cushion in a Bond Street window.
The intellectual gentleman again referred to the
Russian Ballet. And Mrs. —— said that if she had
her time over again she would marry Jem Johnson,
and make him sing the butterfly song over and over
again on summer evenings in her Italian garden till
she perished of emotion.

Many other songs followed, brief, mostly, just
little thoughts sufficiently expressed in a single verse.

E

One beautiful little lyric I remember especially, sung to a most mournful and appealing tune, which ended on a high, sustained, soft note :

> Stowaway !   Stowaway !
>   I see you hidin' ;
> Stowaway !   Stowaway !
>   Come out of yo' corner.
> Stowaway !   Stowaway !
>   I'se rowin' dis boat,
>   I'se rowin' dis boat,
>   I'se rowin' dis boat,
> An' you can't go over Jordan,
> You can't cross over Jordan to-day,
>   Stowaway !

I did not note down any more words, but remember a few titles, such as : *Ole Noah Bought a Shoe ; Shem, Ham and Japhet ; Row, Nigger, Row, de Floods am Comin' ; See Dat Moon ? It's Mine ; Where is Yo' Manners, Nigger ? My Gal Makes Candy ; All Good Chillun Got Good Mammies ;* and *Come, Lubly Ten.*

The performance continued for an hour and the audience never tired. I enjoyed it myself as much as any one—*but*——

But there kept coming into my mind the picture of some industrious white man, somewhere about 42nd Street, New York City, pouring out the soul of the negro in primitive verse at fifty dollars a line. And afterwards, when I saw George (who has recently begun to write) deep in converse with Mr. Jem Johnson——

George denies the charge. Well, well. Anyhow, the party was a great success.

ODD LOTS

I

A VERY BAD FOX

HERE is an old Monday's *Times*. If you have a feeling for good words and the poetry of names, you must never miss the hunting-reports of *The Times* on Monday. This week in these two columns there are recorded the proceedings of twenty-eight different 'hunts' and all these jolly little paragraphs are full of fine and curious names, the names of the English countryside, such names as novelists and poets despair of inventing, and, despairing, borrow from the Ordnance Map. While we read how a fox 'saved his brush' (as the quaint phrase has it) at Polloky's Gorse or Darrington Whin; how hounds were beaten at Woodmancroft and Buckhorn Weston, Bathingwell, Spaceyhouse Whin, Tarporley, Seagry Wood, Stank Whin, Hannington Hanging, Foggathorpe, Tranby Croft and Murky Hill, Childswickham, Nicker Bush, Ginger-bread and Trewhitt's Gill—fields, woods and valleys, hills and dales, all the geography and most of the history of our land seem to float before the eyes. And were these columns concerned with the adventures of lovers instead of the adventures of foxes on Saturday afternoons they would read like the best agricultural literature.

So I for one shall not discourage the publication of these accounts, whatever those low fellows, the sentimentalists, may say about their subject-matter.

As to that, there are arguments on both sides. Very few animals, as some one else has observed, die a natural death ; but fewer still have their deaths recorded in *The Times*. It matters little to the majority of mortals what happens to them on Saturday, provided it is in the papers on the Monday ; and, though foxes, like the victims of murderers, spring into fame a day too late for them to enjoy it, it would be selfish to deny them their little meed of posthumous publicity. Besides, as the sentimentalists forget, it is admitted on all hands that the fox enjoys the sport as much as any, if he is not killed. And this is proved by the fact that, having once escaped, in most cases they join in the hunt on a later occasion with even greater alacrity.

That Saturday, I calculate, no fewer than fifty-eight foxes had fun. Of these no more than sixteen were actually killed and torn to pieces. The remaining forty-two achieved less honour, but had the technical satisfaction of saving their brushes, after periods of anxiety and exertion varying from fifteen minutes to two or three hours. Nearly all, however, had good notices, though, reading between the lines, not all of these, I fear, deserved them. It was the day of an eclipse of the sun, and we may suppose that some devil of perversity and insolence had entered into the creatures in the presence of that exceptional event. At any rate there seems to have been no form of cunning and duplicity from which they shrank on Saturday week. The Brocklesby Hunt, for example—the Brocklesby had a great deal to put up with. Hounds ran their first fox (from Squire HAIGH's covert) for forty minutes, and were then beaten, after having marked their fox to ground. They lost a second (from Grainsby Hall covert), after it had kept them running in rings for thirty minutes. Mortified by these rebuffs, however, they made short work of Number Three, who came from Hell Furze, proceeded to some farm-buildings and was there destroyed. Number Four, a cowardly animal, took refuge in a tree in Grainsby Hall gardens. However, it is recorded that he was dislodged from the tree and hunted for forty minutes, sometimes very fast, and finally escaped under cover of darkness. So that, of these four, no fewer than three saved their brushes.

But the tale is endless. The V.W.H. seems to have suffered infinite inconvenience through the folly and bad feeling of a fox from Raglan's Copse, which deliberately crossed and recrossed the river Cole and finally beat hounds at Highmoor. There were others that, not content with climbing trees, swung right-handed over railways and canals and race-courses, bore left-handed over golf-links, took refuge in sand-pits and rifle-ranges, and spared no pains or trickery to save their brushes—and indeed their lives. The Cottesmore's only fox of the day not only crossed a railway but, turning right-handed for Wing, deliberately took hounds over the very bad scenting ploughs to Glaston Gorse, where he had to be given up.

Against these discouragements it is pleasant to be able to set the triumph of the Holderness, who, after a long run through Nut Wood to Waldby and Tranby Croft and back to South Ella, evicted their fox from a wood-pile and killed him without the loss of a hound. The Middleton too, after a glorious run of twenty-four miles, pursued their fox into the locks at Kirkham, where he was successfully drowned.

The chroniclers are rightly sparing of praise, and the Heythrop is the only pack of which it is definitely stated that they met with ' a good fox.' This good fox was honourably ' rolled over ' in the open by Swan Nest, after a run of one hour and forty minutes, and will linger long in the memory of many. *Requiescit in pieces.*

The Mendip's *third* fox (the first two were bolted, went to ground, and were evicted and devoured) narrowly, we feel, escapes the epithet of ' good,' for, after describing two circles and pointing for Elton, he was headed beyond Priddy, and then, seeing reason, chose a good line for hounds, though it is true that, after two hours and five minutes' work, they had to own defeat.

But what are we to think of the Pytchley's day ? Read this, gentlemen.

> ' Hounds found a very bad fox at Braunston Gorse, who hung about the outskirts of Daventry and eventually escaped.'

No more is known of this animal, or, at any rate, recorded, than is contained in that pregnant sentence. But it is black reading, gentlemen. Had he had the slyness to climb a tree or slink into a wood-pile, had he but run across a railway or dived into a canal, had he but shown one spark of a sense of his position, the chronicler, we may be sure, would have given him his due. But no, he was content to ' hang about '—to hang about and spoil sport. And we can imagine the wretch, lurking from hole to hole, from hedge to hedge, and caring not a pin what pleasure he might have given to others by the simple act of emerging into the open and running rapidly away across a line of country convenient for a pursuit by horsemen.

Well, well, he escaped. But there are some things more precious than life itself, let me tell you, old fox. You escaped, but you have paid your penalty—you have suffered the last, most shattering doom of modern civilization—you have had a bad Press. And as long as the men of our day ride out to Staverton and Thrupp, to Daventry and Braunston, in the copses, in the spinneys, in the whins and in the smoking-rooms, when one Englishman of those parts says to another : ' Do you remember the 24th of January, 1925 ? ' they will not speak of the eclipse of the sun, they will speak of *you*. They will open their diaries, or search the tablets of their minds, or simply take from their pocket-books a cutting from *The Times*, and they will say : ' Yes, I remember ; that was a very bad fox. No gentleman.'

II

MY MESS

COPIES of the original MS. of Mr. Arnold Bennett's *The Old Wives' Tale* have been published at a high figure. They are worth it. I have been privileged to see the original, and it is *the* wonder of the world. So neat, so precise, so rarely marred by erasion or alteration, so beautiful, it is more like a priest's copy of a traditional religious work than the original record of a creative masterpiece. I have recently referred to some of my own old MSS., and I find them equally remarkable, but for different reasons. Not only did Mr. Bennett know exactly what he wanted to say and how he was going to say it ; but it seems that while he wrote that book no one rang him up and left messages, no one called about the rates, no one made it necessary for him to do elaborate sums or draw pictures or monograms ; and no other master-pieces occurred to him while he was at work upon *The Old Wives' Tale.* Moreover he wrote legibly in ink, and wrote in prose ; I write a sort of intoxicated shorthand, in pencil. I have found a few fragments in old note-books which make it clear that Mr. Bennett's method is quite different from my own. For instance, here is a page or two taken at random from the MS. of the poem ' I like them fluffy.'

<pre>
                Some like them little and sweet
                                proud
                Some like them tall and severe
                Some like them stuffed with conceit
                And To some the shy virgin is dear
                                damsel
huffy   And some of the love the whole crowd.
stuff   Some will insist upo grace
                And others are kee o the pelf
snuffy   But t take a particula case
                        I dislike* them fluffy myself
        But I like them fluffy I freely conf
            With eyes that are like   a pretty blue dress.

    Victoria 7203
                Tell Gwen the aunts
                will come to tea
</pre>

With golden hair fly	With clouds of fair	With golden fly
Like clouds	hair	Like the moon in a
And l t seem so	Like Love-in-a-Mist	The sun in a
' You must kiss	And lips that declare	mist
me	' I want to be kissed	seem crying

* Since this poem was published many of my higher-browed friends have found fault with my morals, taste and general out-look. The original MS. shows, to their confusion and my own intense surprise, that the original intention of the work was absolutely worthy. So there !

With fluffy soft cheeks
Like plums on a wall
And what I may call
I like them fluffy   A fluffy soft heart
With no brains   And no brains at all

Brains are all right in their place
But I find it

You are a leader-writer on *The Daily Herald*.   Write a short
leading article of not more than 300 words entitled ' Autumn '
and leading up logically to an appeal for the nationalization of
the means of production distribut   and exc

Chiswick 2710
I will be Bohemian I will

$$3 : 9 : : x : 64$$
$$9x = 182$$
$$182$$
$$\overline{}$$
$$x = 9$$
$$x = 2$$

Can Lavender have tea with the Rowntrees ?
Dont let's go to the dogs to-night
For mother will be there

Some like a girl
Who cares if the charmer's well-read   red
the Society
And some like a shingle or crop
But I don't care what

Who cares what she's got in her   head
  If she's plenty of hair on the top
I sat with a girl on a bench
But every young woman one meets
  Has even less hair than she's heart
                    quotations from Keats
  And asks for one's views about Art
I like them fluffy   I gently reply
                bold as
  And so when I meet a young thing

Alas ! that so many one meets
    Tell Gwen the geyser

      Riverside 3766
Brains are all right in their place
  But I find it
        24 Upper Cheyne Row
        Better be broke by a blonde
          Than bored by a brainy brunette

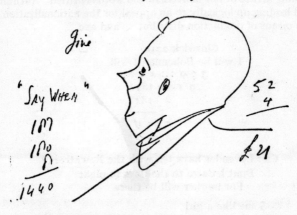

But I do like them fluffy I do
  Give me the radiant
    Who lives on the Chocolate Box
I like them fluffy I   it's a bad taste

With a fluffy   and   flower at   waist
   Brains are all right in their place
     But oh what a shock to the heart   PAY
       If a lady   embrace <u>GAS</u>
         To express her   Art
         To enquire
Or is constantly giving her views
On a Czecho-Slovakian play
    And To-day as I paused on t brink
            annoyed
Whe   She sighed and said ' What do you think
            FREUD
Park 8075   Trout   Friday w'out fail
   Not huffy or stuffy not tiny or tall
     But fluffy just fluffy with no brains
    I like them fluffy I gently replied
Mortimers will be there 4.30 but can you bring a racquet
they can't come to supper thank god
   With downy soft eyebrows and artful blue eyes
           highbrows   despise

$$\frac{5000 \times \overset{5}{60}}{12} = 2500$$

$$20)\overline{2500} \atop 125$$

$$\frac{125}{100} \times 10 = £125 \times £12$$

INSURANCE

   I wish I was horribly rich
With fluffy complexion like plums on a wall
And   at all
   I will be Bohemian I swear
   But I should like a breath of fresh air

There must, I suppose, have been other stages before the final draft was reached, but they will never be published, for I cannot find them. There *was* a final version, I know, but how much less exciting! It began :

Some like them gentle and sweet,
    Some like them haughty and proud,
Some of us like them *petite*,
    And some of us love the whole crowd :
Some will insist upon grace
    And some make a point of the pelf,
But, to take a particular case,
    I do like them fluffy myself.
I like them fluffy, I freely confess,
With fluffy blue eyes and a fluffy blue dress,
With fair fluffy hair, like Love-in-a-Mist,
And lips that declare, ' I want to be kissed,'
With fluffy soft cheeks, like plums on a wall,
With a fluffy soft heart, and no brains at all.

It went on :

Some like a girl that's well read——

But, no. Enough. Or even too much.

III

A FUNNY QUARTER-OF-AN-HOUR

IF, reader, you chanced to hear poor old Haddock broadcast not long ago, an explanation is due to you. It may have crossed your mind that Haddock was not that night exactly his normal ray-of-sunshine self. He was not. But if you can imagine the sensations of a ray of sunshine which is shut up in a soda-water bottle covered with grey velvet and told to scintillate through the cork, you may begin to understand why.

I am an old friend of the B.B.C., and I have always moved about that humming mountain of activity most reverently, feeling as a mortal might have felt who strayed upon the heights of Olympus. The halls and stairways are thronged with gods, Beings in constant touch with millions of invisible earthworms. Any man you meet in the lift may have come fresh from harnessing a nightingale or a thunderstorm. He may have been listening to the heavy breathing of a boxer in Philadelphia, or re-laying a South American earthquake to Glasgow ; and Heaven knows what he may be up to next. The company of such Beings makes a nice-minded man not hilarious but humble.

And always before I have seen the gods gathered together in quantities, and in a fashion almost human. There has been a large grey room with numbers of Shapes tiptoeing here and there before the altar and exchanging strange silent godlike signs with fingers and faces. I have marvelled at the Noise-god, who sits apart upon a sofa, and when the hero cries : ' Give me the letter,' stealthily approaches the sacred microphone and rustles two pages of *The Times*, or clinks a mighty bag of metal when the servant takes a bribe. And there has been in the background a great orchestra, silent, waiting, holding their breath and their trombones ; and there have been stray mortals present like myself, and in spite of the awe and the hush, a pleasant atmosphere of celestial camaraderie. In that atmosphere, I feel, I might almost have given a very distant imitation of a ray of sunshine. But it was not to be.

The first Being who greeted me was gracious and charming.

' What do you want me to do ? ' I asked.

' We want you to read some funny poems,' he said. ' Have you written any funny poems ? '

' I used to think so,' I said. ' But I do not think

they will sound very funny in the ether. I question whether Manchester will raise a chuckle.'

' That will be splendid,' he said cheerfully. ' Come along.'

' And I can't read,' I added.

' That's fine,' he said. ' Come along.'

' But it is conceivable,' I continued, ' that I might be inspired to make some funny remarks between the poems, if that would help.'

' Have they been submitted to the Director of Education ? '

' No.'

The Being gave me a pained look and a brief address, explaining that a funny remark not previously approved by the Beings in Council would be out of order and tantamount to blasphemy.

I was then wafted into a small cell, where a Second Being, as charming as the First, took me under his wing.

The cell was hung with grey velvet. I sat before a desk, from the top of which there protruded a red electric-light bulb, while over it was hung a frightening little microphone, like some poisonous spider just about to drop, and the most terrifying notice I ever saw :

> When the Red Light
> is showing
> **THE WORLD**
> can hear you.
> If you Cough or Rustle your
> Papers
> you will
> **DEAFEN**
> Thousands of People.

I sat numbed and dazed before this legend, waiting for the Red Light to shine.

The Being waited behind me.

I did not feel at all funny.

Stealthily I arranged my funny poems on the desk, holding my breath, fearful that the Red Light would suddenly shine, and at some incautious respiration of mine ten thousand citizens fall prostrate on their hearths with shattered ear-drums.

There was a large clock on the wall. It had a great red hand which ticked rapidly round. 9.30. No Red Light. We waited.

9.31. Still no Red Light.

I thought of the waiting millions.

I felt less funny than ever.

9.32.

9.33. . . .

Suddenly a man burst in at the door and said shortly : ' You're in the wrong studio.'

Wildly I gathered up my bundle of fun, dropped a few stray gems on the floor and galloped after the Second Being down an interminable passage. We barged through a swing-door, dropped a little more fun and came to a part of Olympus which appeared to be under construction or repair. I seem to remember clambering over a ladder and found myself, sadly out of breath, in a larger cell than the first, entirely surrounded by a similar scheme of grey velvet.

The Second Being rushed to the desk and in a majestic whisper said : ' LONDON CALLING.' So may have Jove, looking down from Olympus on his earth-worms, whispered a fretful sigh, and lo ! there was thunder through the earth and terror in every heart.

He then introduced me as Haddock, the well-known ray of sunshine—a few words only, but they carried a distinct suggestion that Haddock was bubbling with fun, that in a moment or two the ether would be alive with laughter, that Haddock was about to EXHILARATE Thousands of People !

Then he gave way to me and I found myself alone with the detestable hanging spider and the red lamp and the awful notice and the grey velvet and what was left of my bundle of fun. No human limb or feature in sight, no friendly sound of man, nothing but grey velvet and a silence like the tomb.

I did not feel at all funny.

I began to read the poem called ' Sausage and Mash.' I seemed to have picked up some other person's voice —some voice I had never heard before, and that not a nice one. And as I read the poem called ' Sausage and Mash ' my mind flew back, as the mind of a murderer flies back to the scene of his crime, to the day on which I wrote it. I remembered how funny I had thought it then, how excruciating, how true. Gad ! how it amused me then ! It did not seem to me to be very funny now. I did not feel that Glasgow was shaking its sides over ' Sausage and Mash.' Nay, I seemed to hear thousands of sharp little clicks as Thousands of People disconnected their machines.

I reached the end of ' Sausage and Mash.' I looked attentively at the spider and listened. Not a hand ! Not a giggle ! The World gave no sign. I said to myself : ' Hang poetry ! Hang the Director of Education ! I am going to make a funny remark. The World will expect it.'

I looked behind me for the Second Being, my mouth

open and on my lips a brilliantly laughable remark. My mouth closed again. The Second Being was not there.

No one was there. Nothing was there. Only the grey velvet and the Red Light and the spider and the silence. Suddenly all the fun had gone out of my remark. And if you, Reader, maintain, Reader, that you could have made that funny remark to a mechanical spider in a vacuum of grey velvet, all I can say is that I invite you to try it.

I began the second funny poem. And as I read I thought sad thoughts. I thought of this strange new voice of mine booming out through a million ornamental loud-speakers in a million boudoirs and bedrooms and bars, and no one paying the smallest attention to it. I thought of the chattering throng in the Private Saloon at ' The Black Lion,' happily discussing boats and tides and murders and what-not, and poor old Haddock's admirable verse flowing unheeded from between those two bottles of Vermouth on the shelf, and of poor old Haddock being funny all by himself in a velvet cell— and I nearly laughed. But it flashed through my quick mind that if a cough could DEAFEN thousands a laugh would kill a million. So I sobered down.

And I read on, sadder and sadder, for fifteen mortal minutes. The Second Being stole in again, but I had no heart now to make my funny remark. I read on. And half-way through the last poem an awful thing happened. *I wanted to sneeze.*

At once I realized the full horror of the situation.

At all costs I must not deafen the World. I read on in strangled halting tones, I read on with a potato in my throat. I read on holding my nose. There was

never such heroic fun before.   And in the very last
verse there happened a still more awful thing.

I did sneeze. . . .

And as I sneezed I saw millions of my countrymen
shattered, shrieking, insane, upon their hearthrugs ;
I saw panic and death at ' The Black Lion ' ; I saw the
survivors scribbling furious postcards of protest ;
I saw myself the common enemy of the Radio World.

I opened my eyes and breathed again.   *The Red
Light was out.*   The World was safe.

But exactly when, I wonder, did they turn the light
out ?

IV

THE %

THis artiple, wich i am typling is theresul t of a bhet
or wager ; I was talkingto my frind MR ST john eR-
        the bramatic CRitic ?
VINe∧good litrary talk too ahout the price of stalls and
wether one o ught to smoke popes at a highh brow
  play and soon so on. when suddenly hee let out in that
shy way heha-s, you know like a vioiolet opening for
I moment on a foggyday, that he typesall his workk

—i dont mean that he wites it downfirst an then hypes
it bot he composesit 8&69¼ if yu can call his kind of
    ritingcom posing, straigt onto the lypewriterlike a
                    r
 a MAN imp∧opervising on the pianano ; ? ; SO i said
of HOURSE that explains how you write the awaful
   mUCK you do — — for this is how literarary pople
talkk wen thy gettogetherin a restorant½ and the

bgreat beutyofthe typlwriteris thatby the juvicious
use of ¾@o¼CAPS you can make your insultts much mor
  emk emkh empatic,i mean wat I SAID was
  MUCk no,; 7¾? no Muck no damit MUCK ! ! ? emph-

atically like That ; well he wass tongutied if you cani-
magi ne that i think his mouth was fuull ; SO i said
i bet i could'n''t write a THINg like thatandhe said
kin dlyof coursse i could. to tell you te truth i have
    nefer rellly mustered this macine before but i said
  that i would typl an ESSaY on The DRamtic Critic
                                    already
  and asfarasi canseei i i I have won my bet ∧ becase
allthough my ttevn my teckn my techniqure is
  improving my ususual pek pello peLLUCID style
  has agandonedme already? you see there are two
allreadies in thesa me sentencealready ; FATal.   ''—

  BUT now i will pul myselftohether?⅓£ WELL the
only question is is is or is is not libellus to say ofa
man thak heisa aramatic critic,. yu see i was once a
dram. crit. myself@ it hapened this way----- i met a
strange EDDitor at l unch & he said ¾Why dont you do
thetheatre for us Our mans gone intoo a Home¾ I
said ¾No thanhks i dont wantto go into a HOMe¾
Behides ; i do'nt know anythinganout acting or duse
dam Duse, and as for hakespeare the man is a CLosed
  book tome' he said t¾that's capital
  JUstwhatwewantyou 'll bringa fresh mind to it¾ i
said i Wont do ithe said youll go tothe WHIPS ofS In
tomorrow¾ & by jove he was right. . . ,
    wellibroughtafreshmindtoit Ogolly lookat that.
  but in less than 6 months my mind was likea cargo
  from the argentine when the rebriger-ating:macinery

breaks down. i do'nt know if it was consstant associo-
ciation with bromatic critics or whabut my hole soul
was horrupted ; ;

WHEn i began i was an absout absolut christian
bot before long i I was sououred ? andbelieveme there
is nothingvinegars aman so surely as seeing3or4funny
plays a WEEk ! ? ! i never said a word about duse or
bernhardrdt but i thought of ever y authorasa crimina
land evry actoras an accessry in the first degree i hate-
d thesightof a HALLOfpleasure ,and as for farces i used
tototter home and cry, so you will never hear me
blime blame the critics for the waythe y behave ;

Indeed i hympathise with them, theonly difference be
tweenus is thati had the decencyto giveit up BUT
thereit isand if the men cant get any other employ.
ment (i'm imploving dontyou think¾ and as i i i I IIII
II said to stjohn having begun life i n that line myselg
it wuld ill become mei said to throw slones at men

who have got no furth-er BETides they ar such sensitive fellows and as I said to ST John (I am impro-

vink¾ rather cleverly i thought scratch a criti c i said
Sratch a critic and you find a martyr) Ha.; !

so i want to keep this ESSAy on a compasassion-
ate note. & per£ and perhaps asi am typlng i can best
express this grop graphically ; Well, youwatch the
poorr critics slinking slinking intothe sTalls hatingever
ybodyalllaloneandmydearsucholdfashonddressjackets ;
like this

%   %   %   %   %   %   %

loook at them, always in ones.   Did youever see any-
thinf qute so dppressing ; Yousee they have absololu-

lutely NOFriendsinfact i hear mostof the m have No
private li fe at alltheyjustliveforthe THEOTRe ;
    butof hourse the jundiced author gets aveery
dfferent impression?k whenhe peeps down from his
boxatthestallshe thinks he seesthis

```
%/%/% %/%/%/% %/%/% %          %/%/%/%/%/% %/%/% £
%/%/£ %/%/%/%/£ %/%            %/%/%/%/%/% %/%/%/%
£  %/%/%/%/%/%/%/ %/%/%        %/%/%/%/%/%/%/%/%/%
%/%/%/£ %/%/%/%/£ £            %/%/%/%/%/£ £/%/%
%/%/% %/%/%/%/%/%/%            %/%/£/%/%/%/%/%/%
```

    the£s of corse represent the pople whohhave paid
fo r their seats, the cuple by the gangway are siralfred
butt and MR BASil dEan ; the others are critixcs
    and then duuringthe bogscene the BIG scene in the
second ACt the wretched authr peeeps downandhe
thinks h e sees thi s$\frac{3}{4}$

```
%      %      %.          %/%              £
    £        £          %
£
      £          £ £  %/%  %        £ £
    %/%        %              £
@-%/5£3  0994  &9
```

    and the pooor foolthink s theyhave allgotogetherat
last in the ba foyer ;

```
%/%/%/%/%/%/%/%/%/%/%/%/%
%/%/%/%/%/%/%/%/%/%/%/%/%
```

BUTITisnt true its a libbel though one or 2 may
haveslippedout to telephone their EDDitors to keep
 morespaacefortheplay,of cours e ; iknow it''s alibelbe-
cuse atthe end you allways seee them slllinkingaway

totheir horribel office s still in Ones and and and not
inthe least convivivia-l,like this)

%   %   %   %   %   %

    isn't it gastly ; ANyone whohas been a Damaticcrit
-tic could tell the authr thatits the lastthinginthe
world tomakeamanconvival and the propoportion that
goes into HOmes is relly infint inginit infinide simal$\frac{3}{4}$

    so the authormust cheeer upan one dayhe willbe a
rich drammatist andbe asked out to dinnerb y the
CRITi'cs CIrCLE''''''

                   %   %
            £   %
        %   %
       %   %
       %   %
        %   %
         %   %
          %   %
           %%

    soletus finishon this note of comhassion. as i said to
stjohn o Lord no CAPitals ! wen i saw that his mouth
was full I think Of A Critic as i / i i I thinkofa poor
washer-woma n whoo spen ds allher li fe passing thrug-
hher hands the the enbia the emv the enviable pose-

    ssions of butter i mean better men, and if she varies
the monotony by pickingholes in them well who can
blame her : THen stJohn opened n his mouth and
shily said 2 $\frac{3}{4}9\frac{1}{2}7$;—$\frac{1}{4}$ 2 two columns of theobserver so
i came home and practisd typlng tilli attaind the
abslute mustery of the intrument which you see ;

    Howeveri still maintain thatit plays the duce the
DEuce with my style ?   A. $\frac{3}{4}$. H.

SUBURBAN SCENES

I

BUYING A BOAT

LAUGH at us if you will, but in Suburbia we do see life. Your garish, artificial, West-End existence may be strange to us; but here in Hammersmith we are daily face to face with the simple, elemental, healthy forces of Nature.

In spring, for example, when we are not thinking about white-washing and grass-seed and garden-chairs and the other delights of the Season, we are thinking about boats. Either we are preparing to buy a boat, or we are preparing to sell a boat, or we are assisting our neighbour to buy (or sell) a boat. Who is there in your gilded Belgravia who opens the Season by buying (or selling) a boat? I do not mean a yacht. I mean a boat. A simple, natural, healthy, elemental thing. About twelve feet long.

Passing the ferry a week or two ago I observed upon the mast of one of the boats which are moored there the notice ' FOR SALE.' She is a grey-painted, dingy and elderly craft, built for speed rather than picnics, and with very little lying-down space. To my knowledge she has been lying there for years, and I have never given her a moment's thought before. The notice ' FOR SALE ' however, inflamed me (before now the notice ' FOR SALE ' upon a boat has inflamed the whole of Hammersmith).

Unhappily I was not at the moment in the position to buy another boat.

' The very boat for Badger,' I said to myself.   Badger has no boat.   He ought to have a boat.   He *shall* have a boat.

I approached old Joe, one of the three elderly watermen who mysteriously exist upon a single ferry and the hire of a few rowing-boats.   They never seem to be in want of work or the price of a beer ; and they never seem to be working.   Now and then they enter a ferry-boat, and slowly, painfully, with many remarks about the tide and about the weather, propel a passenger or two across the river.   For the rest they sit against a wall, as Joe was sitting, contemplate Eternity and discuss (when possible) the buying and selling of boats.

' Good afternoon, Joe,' said I.

' Afternoon, sir,' said old Joe gloomily.   ' Fine tide to-day, sir.'

' Yes,' I said, ' it 's a big tide.'

' Making up very fast with the east wind be'ind 'er,' said he.

' Yes,' I said, ' it 's making up fast.'

' Be a bigger tide than yesterday, I dare say,' said old Joe hopefully.

' I shouldn't wonder,' I said.

(In Hammersmith and Chiswick we devote large sections of the year to this kind of conversation.)

' What do they want for that boat ? ' I inquired, judging that the subject of the tide was nearly exhausted.

A gleam of real interest quickened in the dull old eyes.

' What boat 's that ? ' he said, with an air of surprise.

' The *Bluebell*.'

' The *Bluebell* ? Ah ! I believe 'e'd let 'er go for ten pounds,' he said. ' And she's cheap at that,' he added, spitting (a sure sign that he was lying).

' Who does she belong to ? ' (Yes, I know that there are grammatical objections to that sentence, but that is what I said.)

' Young-feller-name-o'-Thompson.'

' And why's he selling her ? '

' Couldn't 'andle 'er. 'E don't know no more about sailin' a boat than I do about a sewin'-machine. An' 'e wants the money. Take less than ten, I dare say.'

' Do you know anything about her ? ' I said. ' What's her history ? '

The old man boldly met my gaze (a sure sign that he was about to lie).

I have had occasion before to comment on the corrupting influence exerted by those two noble and beautiful things, the horse and the boat, on the characters of men who have to deal with them in the way of sale or exchange. In this case, though, there was no reason to suspect that old Joe had any direct interest in the sale of the boat. He simply wished that the boat should be sold ; the pure and unselfish wish of the longshoreman that the property in all boats shall pass as often as possible, so that the interest of life and the conversation of the shore may be eternally renewed and kept alive.

' I've known 'er for years, sir,' he said. ' She's the quickest little boat below locks. Or above,' he added, ' for 'er size.' And he continued to meet my gaze.

I know old Joe. And old Joe knows me ; and he knows that I know him. And he knew that I knew that this was not the whole truth about the *Bluebell*.

But he also knows that I know the rules. He is my friend. But there are neither friends nor enemies on the pitiless floor of the Boat Exchange. There are only buyers and sellers, and all those not immediately interested are on the side of the seller. And I knew that all the complex forces of modern civilization, concentrated into one force, would not drag from Old Joe the whole truth about the *Bluebell*. For, if it were otherwise, how is the property in boats ever to pass, and how is the interest of life and the conversation of the shore to be perpetually renewed and kept alive ?

' I see,' I said, and left him.

I went to see Badger, who was very busy drawing a daffodil. ' I think I've found you a boat,' I said. ' The very thing for you.'

' I don't want a boat,' he replied.

' It's a bargain,' I said, ' if it's all right.'

' Most things are,' he answered. ' Go away.'

I am not to be put off from a kind action merely by rudeness. It took me some time to persuade Badger (*a*) that he wanted a boat and (*b*) that this was the kind of boat he wanted. But I did it.

The following Saturday afternoon saw Badger and Mrs. Badger, and Mr. Thompson and me, aboard the *Bluebell*, and Mr. Thompson hoisting the sails for inspection. And from the shore the three old ferrymen greedily observed us. Mr. Thompson was a dismal young man, who had arrived from a neighbouring suburb on a motor bicycle, evidently hated all boats, and loathed the *Bluebell* with a deadly loathing.

I had warned Badger not to be too particular about the sails, for sails can be repaired or replaced, and the hull (if sound) was worth the money alone.

The sails, as they went up, showed how right I had been. They hung, like the tatters of a stage beggar, flapping picturesquely in the breeze.

We turned our gaze downwards, where a sheet of water lapped about our boots. Badger knows nothing about the boat trade, and he kept on asking direct unwarrantable questions, such as ' Does she leak ? ' Mr. Thompson said there had been a great deal of rain lately and guaranteed that all the water in the boat was rain. We sat and stared at it, trying to gauge if it was rising or not. Mrs. Badger inclined to the opinion that it was, but she knows nothing about boats.

I suggested to Badger in a whisper that he should offer Mr. Thompson five pounds for the *Bluebell*, subject to her being ' tight,' as to which we should have to satisfy ourselves during the week. Mr. Thompson replied sourly that he had no time to waste ; that he could not come to Chiswick *every* Saturday ; that he would sell the boat for ten pounds ; that he would be losing twenty pounds at that ; that maybe some of the upper seams were a little dry ; that there had been much sunshine lately, but——

At this point Badger, who knows nothing about boats, plunged his hand into the water and pulled from the *Bluebell's* frame a large strip of tow.

The water rose like a flood. The boat began to sink. We left her rapidly.

Mr. Thompson mounted his motor bicycle and crossly rode away.

By this time the whole waterside knew that the property in the *Bluebell* was *not* to pass. Old Joe approached me, confidential and obsequious.

' If I were *you*, sir,' he said, ' I wouldn't have nothing

to do with that boat, sir. I wouldn't say this to every one, sir, but I'm speaking to you as a friend. She's rotten, that's what she is. What we calls " nail-sick," sir. " Nail-sick,"' he repeated with enjoyment. ' There's not a sound plank in 'er. But she's that plugged up with putty and tow and red lead an' all, so's a gentleman like you wouldn't know the difference, I dare say. Rotten, that's what she is,' he continued with enthusiasm. ' I've known that boat for forty years, sir. Mr. Potts give fifty pounds for 'er. An' after that Mr. Davids 'ad 'er for a bit—Mr. Davids at the brewery. 'E give twenty, and 'e sold 'er for nine——'

' What did Mr. Thompson give for her ? ' I inquired curiously.

' She was left to 'im in a will,' said Joe. ' A legacy like.'

' Ah ! ' I said. ' It's funny, Joe, you didn't tell me all this the other day.'

But old Joe did not seem to hear.

' Well, sir,' he said, ' don't say I didn't warn you. I'm surprised,' he added, ' at a gentleman like you wasting your time over a boat like 'er.'

' Yes,' I said, ' that's funny too.'

II

TENNIS WITH TRUNDLE

I DO not wish it to be understood that the events which I shall now describe were in any way exceptional. The same sort of thing has always happened to me whenever I have played lawn tennis on a Saturday

at our local club, and I believe that it happens to
all who play on Saturdays at all suburban tennis-clubs ;
and I suppose that it will continue to happen until the
Home Office intervenes.

The club has two long lines of courts, which we will
call the North and the South Courts, and they are
divided by a single net, which is insufficiently high
and has more holes in it than the manufacturers
intended. Between one North Court or one South
Court and another, however, there is no net, so that
a member, if he would, might lie down and roll along
the ground from Court 1 to Court 12, or from Court
13 to Court 24, without obstruction.

I played on Saturday with Trundle and his wife and
an agreeable young lady friend of their's, a Miss Betty
Bright. Trundle is a barrister, precise and careful in
every little thing, a family man and never reckless in
matters of expenditure. Miss Betty Bright, I gathered,
came of a family more affluent than either the Trundles
or the Haddocks, and she seemed to be of a fine, free,
careless habit in body and mind.

If you are fond of lawn tennis there is nothing jollier
than a jolly game of lawn tennis on a jolly afternoon
at a jolly club. The sun shone and I was to play with
Betty Bright. I walked on to Court 2 whistling and
swinging my racket and blithely executing imaginary
' chop ' volleys. There was some little delay before
we actually began, because Trundle was dissatisfied
with the height of the net, and while he was still
strongly working at the handle the wire broke and the
net collapsed altogether. I stopped whistling. Trundle
sent for the groundsman and showed him how to
mend the wire with pieces of string. The groundsman

mended it in this way several times and then went
off to fetch another net.

Meanwhile play was proceeding a little wildly on all
the other courts, and Betty Bright and I were straining
at the leash. But Trundle sat down quietly and
' marked ' the balls again.

Trundle has six tennis-balls. They did not look
extremely new, but it was clear that they were valuable. Trundle marked them with a special indelible
pencil, first licking his thumb and moistening the
pencil on his thumb. On Saturdays Trundle always
has a blue thumb. On every ball he wrote a large
capital T and a large capital X. ' I add the X,'
he explained, ' because there are so many T's in the
club.'

Trundle threw his racket on the ground, Betty
Bright called ' Roughs,' I called ' Smooths,' and Trundle
said we could have our choice of courts, meaning that
he would like to serve first.

The first game passed off normally. Either Trundle
served a double fault into the net, or his second serve
came over, and Betty Bright or I returned it into the
net in the usual way.

Betty Bright insisted on my serving first. I seized
two balls, loosened my arm with a few swings and
prepared to bamboozle Mrs. Trundle with my American
service.

At this moment a ball struck me in the face. I
picked it up and looked at it. It was marked Q M.
Far away I heard a voice call ' Thank you ! ' ' Not
at all,' I replied, and smote the ball into the air and
in the general direction of Court 15. I was then
winding myself up to serve again when a lady's voice

behind me said : ' Excuse me, but have you a ball marked P ?   P with a little dot ? '   ' Afraid not,' I said confidently, but courteously picked up the balls on the ground and examined them.   ' Afraid not,' I repeated.

' What's that in your hand ? ' said the lady tentatively.   ' Isn't it a P ? '

I looked.   It was a P—a P with a little dot.

I apologized profusely.   The lady smiled sweetly and Trundle called fussily across to her : ' Our balls are marked T X.'

' Our balls are marked P,' she replied—' P with a little dot.'

Slightly shaken, I served.   My American service is erratic at the best of times, and I now struck the ball with the extreme edge of the racket, so that it flew away six courts to the eastward.   We all stood still and watched its progress.   It bounded on and on as though it would never stop, but came to rest at last near the service-line of Court 8.

' I think perhaps you'd better get that at once, Haddock,' said Trundle patiently.

' Oh, no,' protested Betty ; ' do let's go on.'

' It's safer,' said Trundle kindly but firmly.   ' One *loses* balls here.'

Accordingly I wandered off in the direction of Court 8, my eyes glued to the truant ball.   When I had reached Court 6 I saw a lady pick it up and prepare to serve with it.

' Thank you,' I cried feebly, and again wistfully, ' Thank you.   Have you a ball marked T X ?   *Thank you* ! '

The lady did not hear, but nobly served the ball.

Her opponent mis-hit it, and the ball marked T X sailed grandly away to Court 10.

A little dispirited, I resumed the chase. On Court 10 they had just finished a game, and one of the ladies, who was exceedingly beautiful, was collecting the balls. I saw her pick up among others the ball marked T X.

' Excuse me,' I said, approaching shyly and following the ritual, ' but have you by any chance a ball marked T X ? '

She smiled a radiant smile at me and said : ' No, I'm afraid not.'

I knew that the ball marked T X was in her hand. I knew that I should say next : ' Excuse me, but isn't *that* one—— ? '

What I did say was ' Oh ! ' and also ' Thank you.' And I melted away a yard or two. Stronger men no doubt would have acted otherwise, but I did not.

The game began, and I stood at hand, waiting for a chance to pounce on the ball marked T X. Almost immediately it came into action, and without surprise I saw the beautiful lady hit it hard and high over the dividing net to the farther side of Court 16.

I scrambled under the net and *ran* after that ball, braving the wrath of the fierce ' men's four ' who were bounding about on Court 16. This time I was taking no risks.

As my fingers closed at last upon the prize I heard a voice say ' Thank you,' behind me. It was said accusingly by one of the fierce men. ' Sorry ; one of ours,' I stuttered ; and ' Oh ! ' he said suspiciously. I was now far gone. I saw that the man did not believe me. The awful thing was that I found I did not very much care.

However, to propitiate the man, I threw him two of his own balls, as men throw buns to a tiger. And as I did so I noticed with astonishment and horror that *both of them were marked* T X.

Pondering this circumstance, I returned to Trundle. *I might easily have been accused of larceny.*

The set continued, very much as before. Sometimes I was asking other people if they had a ball marked T X, and sometimes other people were asking me if I had a ball marked Q M, or a ball marked S S, or a ball marked A in a large circle. Before very long I knew the initials of every court on the ground. It was clear that no one came there to play lawn tennis. The one idea was to preserve intact the family possessions.

Trundle grew very trying. He had some provocation, I must admit, for Betty Bright, who was not accustomed to this kind of tennis, became very scornful about the precious balls, and sometimes, at the end of a game, she hit them up to Trundle quite wildly, so that one or two bounded over into Court 14. But the patient way in which Trundle always said : ' I say, be careful, Haddock, old man,' was very hard to bear. Meanwhile my game, of course, went quite to pieces ; I played so badly that I stopped saying ' Sorry.'

We were very unlucky with our balls, and at last for all our care we had dwindled down to four—two balls marked T X, a ball marked B with a kind of squiggle under it, and a ball marked A in a large circle. These two were instantly claimed and we were left with two.

' This will never do,' said Trundle testily, with a

hostile glare at the entire club. ' You must be more careful, Haddock, old man.'

A wicked inexcusable thought took hold of me.

' I tell you what,' I said, ' I've an idea they may have some of ours in Court 16. Why don't you go and have a look ? '

Betty Bright and I sat down, and we watched poor Trundle march firmly off to the four fierce men, who were also marked T X. We watched him pick up four of their balls in succession and angrily examine them. He threw one horrid glance at the four fierce men and was just walking away with his captures when one of the men observed him. ' Hi ! ' he cried, just ' Hi ! ' Trundle turned, and the two men faced each other. They entered into a conversation ; they spoke ; they said things. . . .

Oh, dear !

INSINCERE FLATTERIES

I

MACHEATH, M.P.

(*Being a newly-discovered sequel to 'The Beggar's Opera' and 'Polly.' It deals with the life of Captain and Mrs. Macheath on their return to London from the West Indies. From internal evidence we are inclined to think that it is not, as it purports to be, by* JOHN GAY, *but the work of some imitator of a later period.*)

ACT ONE

Scene I.—MACHEATH'S HOME AT CHELSEA.

Macheath. Polly. Filch.

Polly. Husband, why do you sigh? By your melancholy I suspect you have married another wife.

Macheath. Nay, Polly, you wrong me.

Air I.—*The Spanish Shawl.*

When wind and water teases
  To shore the sailors come ;
Though any harbour pleases,
  The dearest port is home.
Hi ! Ho ! Ahoy !
  The dearest port is home.

One kiss, Polly, and I am a man again.

Polly. What—only one ? This is not the Macheath I have married so often.

Macheath. Polly, you are right ; I am not the man I was. These weeks of virtue at home have corrupted my constitution. The air of Chelsea suffocates me. Besides, I am concerned for our expenses. Your routs and dances are well enough for a highwayman who has the means, but they are ruinous to a respectable man of no employment. What do you say, Filch ? Shall we take the road ? or turn pirate again ?

Polly. Ah, Macheath, you promised to stay respectable till Michaelmas.

Macheath. So I will, Polly. It will take time to get the gang together.   [*Exit* Polly.

Filch. There is one other profession which a thief may still pursue without losing his good name. You are become a little portly for the road, Captain, but you may yet be a Member of Parliament.

Air II.—*The Tinker's Wedding.*

Pirates must be young and lusty,
Robbers grow infirm and rusty
    If too long their trade they ply.
Statesmanship's another story ;
Lawyers steal till they are hoary,
    Politicians till they die.

Enter Diana Trapes.

Macheath. Why, who is this ? Death, if it is not Diana Trapes ! Mrs. Trapes, your servant.

Trapes. Lady Diana, Captain, if it pleases you, for I have married a lord and have a fine house.

Macheath. Such a misfortune has sent many a woman to the bad, but I dare swear that Diana Trapes is as charming and virtuous as ever.

Air III.—*Cheapside.*

High or humble, dark or fair,
Wenches ever wenches were,
Fal-de-riddle-fal-al-lay.

Trapes. Captain, I have come upon a matter of business concerning your future.

Macheath. You have brought me no more wives, I hope, for I am very content with my dear Polly, so long as no one shows me a better.

Trapes. No, Captain ; this affair is serious. You must know that among the poorer people there is a certain ill-disposed kind of creature that is in the habit of taking drams to an extraordinary pitch ; and such is the effect upon them that the rich are no longer able to rely upon their industry and devotion as they should.

Macheath. This is strange, Lady Di. For when I have taken a dram I am ready for anything.

Trapes. The poor too are capable of any wickedness to avoid work. And my husband's men so stupefy themselves with ale and spirits that it is as much as he can do to earn a living from their labours. A number of good citizens therefore have formed themselves into a company to put down this beastly traffic. We are called the No Rum Company, and I am the President.

Macheath. Well, Lady Di, this is a pretty topic for conversation, to be sure, and the very thought of what you mention has tickled my fancy. Bring rum, Filch. [*Exit* Filch.

Trapes. Now, Captain, to come to a conclusion, it is necessary for the success of our designs that we should have in Parliament some well-disposed gentleman of known reputation to defend our cause ; and since you came to anchor in Chelsea you have made such a name for piety and good behaviour that our choice has fallen on you.

Macheath. Lady Di, no man has more at heart than I the cause of temperance among the poor ; but things have come to a pretty pass if my private life is to be interfered with. [*Filch brings rum.*

Trapes. Have no fear, Captain. The rich will always be able to satisfy their moderate desires. Your health, Captain. [*She drinks.*

Macheath. Your health, Lady Di. [*He drinks.*

Trapes. But with you at Westminster we will soon stamp out the excesses of the people.

Macheath. Then I am your man. But, Lady Di, do you not think this cloak will sit strange upon a gentleman of my history and connexions ?

Trapes. Why, no, Captain ; your brand plucked from the burning is ever the handiest instrument to beat out a fire.

Air IV.—*Phyllis went to London.*

Dogs delight to bark and bite—
   Wangle-dangle-doo !
When dog eats dog how sharp the fight !
   Wangle-dangle-doo !

Trapes. And now, Captain, if Mrs. Polly is not too handy, I will introduce you to an old friend, who will be overjoyed to hear of your readiness.

Enter Jenny Diver.

Macheath. Jenny, the slut ! (*He kisses her.*) But,

Lady Di, I warned you. I will not be put to the expense of another wife.

Trapes. Indeed, sir, I am not likely to forget this squeamishness. But now that you are to become a statesman you will have employment for her, and plenty.

Macheath. What is this ? Do Members of Parliament have more wives than others ?

Trapes. No, sir, but you will require a secretary. And Jenny can write a letter or deceive a constituent as well as any wench in Sydenham.

Jenny. It is true, sir. I have till late been secretary to a merchant that became a Knight, but I had the misfortune to take his watch while sitting on his knee.

Macheath. Ah, Jenny, you must cast off the old habits if you are to be employed by me ; for if a man may not embrace his secretary without losing his watch, then family life will become impossible.

Jenny. It is cruel for a master to put temptation in the way of his servants. I hope, Captain, that you will not wear a watch.

Macheath. Very well, Jenny. You are employed. But, Jenny, you know my new beliefs. Is your heart in the cause ?

Jenny. Indeed, sir, I do think that rum is an invention of the Devil. I can take nothing but good wine—and brandy when I am sick.

Air V.—*Green Brocade.*

Every pleasure is a sin,
Jill loves ginger, Jack loves gin,
Please your taste whate'er it is,
But save your sinful friend from his.

Enter Polly.

Macheath. Polly, my dear, here is your old friend, Jenny Diver, who has come to stay with us for a year or two.

Polly. You saucy julep ! Out of my house !

Air VI.—*Hop-o'-my-Thumb.*

Polly.	Baggage !
Diver.	Bully !
Polly.	Jackal !
Diver.	Jade !

Polly. Oh, Macheath, send her away. This is the anniversary of our second wedding, and I would be alone with you.

Macheath. My dear, you misunderstand me. I am to go into Parliament, and Jenny is to be my secretary.

Polly. Your secretary ? Oh, Macheath, what new wickedness is this ?

Trapes. You had better make yourself used to the idea, Mrs. Polly, for when he is in Parliament he will want two, and by the time he is a Minister six will not suffice him.

Polly. Wretched Polly ! from the very first you were fated to live in a crowd.

Macheath. But come, Polly, this is no time for repining. There is work to be done, and work for all. Jenny dear, will you at once make ready some kind of plausible Address to win the hearts of my constituents ? Good Filch, acquaint the gang of my intentions, and bid them be ready for any devilry. As for you,

Polly—— Lady Di, for what constituency am I to sit ?

Trapes. For Chelsea, Captain, where you have lived so long and honourably.

Macheath. Then, Polly, put on your black poplin and prepare to impress the women of Chelsea with your virtue and my gallantry. Kiss all babies, but go delicately with the electors. And now, friends, fill, and let us pledge a toast. (*He drinks.*) Down with rum !

All. Down with rum ! And long live our Honourable Member !

Trapes. Down with rum—for the last time, Captain.

[*They drink.*

Air VII.—*Where is Martin ?*

Down with rum that rots our livers !
Let the poor man tap the rivers ;
　　Rum's no drink of mine.
Down with rum, the people's ruin !
Down with beer and down with brewin'—
　　We'll make shift with wine !

[Curtain]

Scene II.—A Street in Chelsea.

Filch and Pirates disguised as Voters.

Pirates. Vote for Macheath ! Down with Drammer !

[*They drink.*

Filch. You shout well, boys. Shout once again with that spirit and the Election is won !

Enter Macheath.

Pirates. Vote for Macheath ! Down with Drammer !

Macheath. Good. But now compose yourselves, for I go to Tite Street to deliver an oration against rum ; and it is your charge to see that such stones as are flung at my head fall wide of the mark.

Pirates. Hurrah !

Macheath. That done, brothers, I shall become again the rascally Drammer, and deliver an oration in praise of spirits at the corner of Swan Walk, where I look to you to defend me from the fury of Captain Macheath's supporters, who are a very villainous sort of creature and violent in their cups.

Pirates. Vote for Drammer ! Down with Macheath !

Filch. Do you think it is wise, Captain, to take upon yourself the dangers and exertions of *two* Parliamentary Candidates at this Election ?

Macheath. Why, yes, Filch, for in this way I have already disposed of all opposition. The electorate are fickle birds, as you know ; but whatever their waywardness one of us is bound to be elected.

Filch. I know your fondness for acting in a double capacity, Captain, and so long as it was a matter of marriage we were ready to follow you ; but we are honourable men, and to stand for both Parties seems to many of us to be not far distant from underhand conduct.

Macheath. This is the first time anything of that nature was laid to my door. On the contrary, my friends, by this device I am able to present both sides to the people with a fairness never surpassed. For if the bold Macheath comes out too strong in argument, as the nimble-witted Drammer I stagger him with a retort. And if the vile Drammer blunders into an error, within the hour Macheath has nailed the lie to the mast. This is the way of all Elections, but it has never been done with such impartiality and good feeling before. Here in Chelsea the Candidates have thrown off all personal ambition and care not which may win, provided only that the truth prevail, which is more than can be said of many boroughs.

Filch. True, Captain; but how can the truth prevail if Drammer be elected? For Lady Di has offered us money to elect Macheath.

Macheath. If the people choose Drammer, then Drammer is right; for the people know what is right, and who am I to go against them? As for your fees, have no fear, for if Lady Diana should fall behind in her duty, I will see to it that Drammer does what is honourable.

Filch. Then, Captain, we are yours; and we hope that the truth will prevail, one way or the other.

Pirates. Hurrah!

Air VIII.—' *Like Cobblers a-stitchin'.*'

By reason, not ruction,
  We soar to the skies;
The means of production
  We nationalize;
While rapture surprising
  We bring within range
By nationalizing
  The means of exchange.*

* These lines are probably a later interpolation. Ed.

Scene III.—Tite Street.

Macheath.   Jenny Diver.   Polly.   Diana Trapes.

Pirates.   A Crowd.

Macheath *on a barrel.*

Macheath. Citizens of Chelsea! I have been nearer hanging than any gentleman here, not for my crimes but for my passions. I have been married three times, not counting baggages, and twice to the same wife. I have been a highwayman and a pirate ; and in ten days I shall be a Member of Parliament.

Pirates. Hurrah !

Macheath. Citizens! I owe my misfortunes to a single circumstance.

Polly. Cruel Macheath !

Air IX.—' *Pop goes the Weasel !* '

The turtle-dove that droops and dies,
    Her grief complaining,
Reproaches yet with startled eyes
    The hunter's feigning.

Macheath. Polly, you mistake me. Citizens ! a man may rid himself of his wives, but rum pursues him to the grave. More men have gone to their ruin through rum than ever went to the cart for thieving ; more men are destroyed by rum than are taken off by the plague. More rum is drunk than water. To work is a poor man's glory, and if you give up your drams you will have more time to work. Citizens, you are a poor lot, but what will you be if you drink water ! You will be rich. When I am in Parliament I shall see to it that you are rich.

Pirates. Hurrah!

Macheath. I am a better man than Drammer. I wish to say nothing to the prejudice of Drammer, for every man has his tastes, and if Drammer chooses to cut purses, that is his own affair. God save the King!

Pirates. Hurrah! Vote for Macheath! [*Exeunt.*

Polly. Husband, how noble a discourse! Tell me it was the thought of your Polly's virtue and constancy that breathed that resolution into your words.

Macheath. All Jenny's work, the slut.

[*He kisses her.*

Polly. Oh, Macheath, though you may weary of my affection, at least you should let me prepare your speeches. From this day forth Polly is your secretary.

Macheath (*aside*). Then Drammer is elected—— Well, my dear, I am delighted. Jenny, you are dismissed.

Jenny Diver. Oh, sir, have pity. I suffer from tedium, like the fine ladies, and after three weeks of politics in your service I am in no mood to pick pockets again.

Macheath. Take my advice and call on Mr. Drammer, who needs a secretary, as I happen to know.

Polly. She shall leave my house to-night.

Macheath. Why, no, my dear; for the fact is this Drammer is little better than a vagabond and has no house. And till he acquires a respectable dwelling I fear that Jenny must remain under our roof. For I know you would not turn the poor girl into the streets.

Polly. Willingly.

Air X.—' *Bristol Maidens.*'

Thus when cuckoo from the nest
    Thrusts the rightful queen,
She, poor bird, with heaving breast,
    Longs to make a scene,
Could she but resist the rough ;
But she is not strong enough.

Scene IV.—SWAN WALK.

Macheath.   Diana Trapes (disguised).   Jenny Diver
Pirates.   A Crowd.

Macheath *on a barrel, disguised as* Drammer.

Macheath.   Fellow-citizens, I am a merchant of
honour, reputation and wealth.

Pirates.   Hurrah !

Macheath.   You have heard to-day an oration from
the lips of the notorious Macheath.   He lies.   God
save the King !

Pirates.   Hurrah !   Vote for Drammer !   [*Exeunt.*

Jenny Diver.   Mr. Drammer, sir, I am a secretary
discharged by the vile Macheath.   I seek employment.
If I cannot get you into Parliament, or any other
place, my name is not Diver.

Macheath (aside).   Jenny, the slut !   You are
engaged.   [*He kisses her.*

Diana Trapes (aside).   It *is* the Captain !   No other
statesman would engage a secretary with so much
ceremony.   Macheath !

Macheath (aside).   Discovered !—Lady Di ? '

Trapes.   You play me false, Captain.   I employed
your services for the No Rum Company.   Have a
care, Captain.   If Drammer wins, Macheath shall hang

Macheath. These apprehensions do you no credit. Come what may, Macheath will finish at the top of the *poll.*

Scene V.—A Polling-Booth.

Macheath (*disguised*). Filch.

Filch. Vote early and often! Ha! 'tis you, Captain?

Macheath. Soft. What news! How often have you voted?

Filch. Nine times, Captain. You are in.

Macheath. Naturally. But in which capacity?

Filch. Macheath wins. The people are captured by his cheerfulness and honesty. They vote in hundreds, dead or alive.

Macheath. This is well. Vote again. [*Exit.*

Scene VI.—An Open Place—Outside 'The George.'

Outside 'The Dog and Thunderstorm.'

Sheriff's Officer. Pirates. A Crowd.

Sheriff's Officer. Macheath is elected.

Pirates. Hurrah!

Enter Macheath, *in the windows of 'The George.'*

Macheath. Citizens! in the hour of victory it is our privilege to be generous. I will tell you why I won. Drammer is no gentleman. God save the King!
[*Exit.*

Pirates. Hurrah!

Enter Macheath, *disguised as Drammer, in the windows of 'The Dog and Thunderstorm.'*

Macheath. Citizens! in the hour of defeat a just

man bows his head with a cheerful grace. I will tell you why I lost. Macheath is no gentleman. God save the King!   [*Exit.*

   Pirates.   He lies!   *Sapristi!*

Air XI.—' *Sweet Myrtle.*'

After battle
Who but cattle
    Crawl upon the ground?
Melancholy
Is but folly;
    Pass the bottle round!

[CURTAIN]

End of Act I.

ACT TWO

Scene VII.—THE HOUSE OF COMMONS : ST. STEPHEN'S HALL.

Jenny Diver.   Diana Trapes.   Filch.   Constituents.
   Pirates disguised as Constituents.   Constables.

   Jenny Diver.   They say the Captain carries all before him in Parliament.

   Diana Trapes.   He is a House of Commons man. The Members love a hearty rogue.

   Diver.   I doubt he will not carry the Bill to Abolish Rum, for they love rum better.

   Trapes.   He will carry anything. He has such a smile and speaks with such an air that no man cares what he says while he is saying it, or remembers what he has said when he has done.   But all feel happier than before.

Diver. There are those here that remember what he said.

Constituents. Ay ! Curse him !

Enter Macheath.

A Constable. Does any gentleman desire speech with Captain Macheath ?

Omnes. Ay ! Curse you !

A Merchant. You promised to put down the poor.

An Ostler. You promised to put down the rich.

A Farmer. You promised to put a duty on corn.

A Mother. You promised bread for the children.

Omnes. Traitor !

Macheath. Gentlemen, have patience. I am the friend of the people, and what I promised I will perform. But you know that in this House I am but one honest man fighting the intrigues of the great. You must give me time.   Look in my eyes, gentlemen. Have I the aspect of one who would deceive you ?

Constituents. Never ! Hurrah ! Long live the Captain !   [*Exeunt.*

Macheath. Ha ! This sort of scum have such long memories that a gentleman can scarce make any promise without inconvenience. Lady Di, your Bill will be read a Third Time to-night ; here's my hand upon it.   What now, Filch ?

Filch. Captain, the boys are discontented concerning this Bill.

Pirates. Ha ! Curse you !

Filch. Noble Captain, we knows you have a holy mission in the matter, and we respects your sentiments, but this Bill will be the ruination of our characters,

for now that we have given up thieving and live respectable on your bounty, we have nothing to do but
drink, and if there is to be no more rum we shall have
no employment at all ; and an idle man, Captain, is
hard put to it to avoid mischief.

Macheath. Honest Filch, the end of rum is the
beginning of mischief. When this Bill becomes law,
you will never lack employment again. Anchor the
sloop off the Terrace, boys, and meet me there at
sundown. Jenny—and you, Filch—a word with you.

[*They confer.*

Scene VIII.—The House of Commons : The Terrace.

Moonlight. A Sloop in the Offing. Jenny Diver.

Enter Filch.

Filch. All goes well within. The Captain will
speak presently. Watch for the lantern and be ready
to play your part.

Diver. It is a very poor part to sit here in the dark
for two hours and throw myself into the river at the
end of it.

Filch. It is all a woman is fit for in politics, or
any other great matter. But I hope the river may
not be necessary. Cry loud enough and all will be
well.   [*Exit.*

Diver. How slowly the hours pass when a woman
is alone ! In such a time the mind turns readily to
love.

Air XII.—' *Twankey dillo.*'

Come, gentle Love,
And we will all the pleasures prove.

Enter a Minister.

Minister (*aside*). A woman, and defenceless, in this spot ! Madam, allow me to conduct you to a place of safety. It is well for you that you are discovered here by a Minister and not by a member of the Opposition.

Diver. Who are you, sir ?

Minister. I am the President of the Board of Trade.

Diver. Then let us sing a catch.

Air XIII.—' *The Deer by Stealth.*'

> Though factions burn and brawl
>   And rancour daily worsens,
>   For all their rage
>   Behind the stage
>   The Parties are but persons,
> And life-long foes together
> Discuss the wine and weather.

Scene IX—THE HOUSE OF COMMONS : THE CHAMBER.

The Speaker. Members. Macheath.

Sir John Straight. Mr. Speaker, sir, this Bill will be an end of the country.   [*He sits down.*

Mr. Druggett. Mr. Speaker, I yield to no man in my zeal for Reform, but this Bill is against Nature, and there is an end of the matter.   [*He sits down.*

Members. Hear !

Mr. Tabbery. I am a chirurgeon, and rum is a sovereign remedy for low spirits. No civilized nation has gone without rum, and is England to be the first ? Was it for nothing that our fathers captured Jamaica ? I am surprised that the honourable and gallant Member for Chelsea should give his name to this Bill—this wicked Bill, this barbarous Bill.   [*He sits down.*

Members.   Hear !

Mr. True.   I am not surprised. Who are the Honourable Members whose names are on the back of this Bill ?   They represent waterside Boroughs, inhabited by low mariners, pirates and smugglers, who have an interest in this Bill.   The Honourable——

Macheath.   Mr. Speaker, on a point of order, sir, I have never been a smuggler.

The Speaker.   Order.   The honourable Member must not say that another Member is a smuggler ; but he may say that his constituents are smugglers.

Members.   Hear !

Mr. True.   The honourable and gallant Member for Chelsea was elected by pirates, smugglers, and longshoremen, and he has a fleet of small sloops and ketches now lying off this Honourable House.   If this Bill is passed there will be more smuggling done than any trade in the kingdom, and Honourable Members who have not the fortune to sit for maritime Boroughs will hardly hold up their heads again.

Macheath.   You are a scoundrel.

Members.   Order !

Mr. True.   Pirate !

A Member.   Horse-thief !

Members.   Cut-purse !—You lie !—'S'death !—Potbelly !

The Speaker.   Honourable Members must speak to the question.

Macheath.   I move that the Question be now put.

[*Jenny Divers cries aloud without.*

Diver (without).   Help !   Murder !   Thieves !

A Member.   A woman in distress!   [*Exit.*
Members.   Villainy!—Lud, what a voice!—A strip-
ling!—Succour the wench!—Ho!   [*Exeunt.*
                    [*Manent* Speaker *and* Macheath.
The Speaker.   The Question is that this Bill be
read a third time.   Will those of that opinion say
' Aye ' ?
Macheath.   Aye !
The Speaker.   Contrary—' No ' ?   I think the 'Ayes'
have it.

Air XIV.—' *King Henry.*'

Young men, be wise ;
Though Woman's eyes
    Are fatal hobbies,
More danger shows
In Woman's ' Noes '—
    Clear the Lobbies !   Clear the
    Lobbies !

Scene X.—THE TERRACE.

Jenny Diver.   The President of the Board of Trade.

Diver.   Pray leave me now, sir.   I would be alone.
The President.   Why, no, Madam, for I would not
abandon you to the mercy of the Whigs.
Diver (aside).   This booby will ruin himself and us
too.   [*Filch shows a lantern.*
                    [*Diver raises a great crying.*
Diver.   Help !   Murder !   Thieves !
The President.   Madam, compose yourself.
Diver.   Wretch !   Ha !   Let me go !
            Enter Members, *in Confusion.*
Members.   What !—Watchman !—Ho !
[*They seize the* President of the Board of Trade.

Diver. The bully offered me discourtesy. How I tremble !

Sir John Straight. This scoundrel shall know the inside of the Tower.

Diver. Stay with me, gentlemen, for I am a timid nature.

Members. Willingly.

Air XV.—' *Old Ned.*'

For faction a fig !
Tho' Tory and Whig
    At hating are hearty,
United we woo,
The Red and the Blue,
    For Love's above Party.

Enter Macheath *with* Pirates.

Macheath. The Bill is carried. By one vote ; but a good one.

Members. What ! Trickery ! Ho !   [*Exeunt.*

Macheath. Jenny, you slut, you were born to be a politician. The Lords will pass the Bill in their sleep, and then we are all rich men. Go, boys, up sail and away, and bring back the sloop as full of liquor as she will take the water. Why, if we do no more than supply the Houses of Parliament we shall be wealthy beyond the dreams of common men. Gentlemen, away !

Pirates. Ha !

Air XVI.—' *The Parson's Wooing.*'

Let Ministers bawl till they burst,
    Let Parliament do as it please—
Our countrymen never shall thirst,

They SHALL have their penn'orth of
    rum !
We'll never be hung for a lamb ;
    While Englishmen sail the wide seas,
Tho' it cost them a guinea a dram,
    They SHALL have their penn'orth of rum,
                                Brave boys,
        They SHALL have their penn'orth of rum !

End of Act II.

ACT THREE

Scene XI.—A ROUT AT VAUXHALL.

Macheath.   Polly.

Polly.   Will you not dance with your Polly, husband ?

Macheath.   You talk like a simpleton, my dove.
We are not here for pleasure, but business ; and the
wife of a statesman must occupy herself with those
who can advantage him.   Here comes Mr. Greville.
Do your duty, my love.   [*Exit.*

Enter The Prime Minister.

The Prime Minister.   Mrs. Macheath ?   And alone ?
Has Society gone mad ?

Polly.   A woman in melancholy is no company
for the gentlemen, sir.

The Prime Minister.   What, melancholy.   Only
tell me the cause and Parliament shall root it up
to-morrow.

Polly.   I suffer in my husband's disappointments.
His expenses are as heavy as his debts, and, though he
has voted with Government these three months, he
holds as yet no office under the Crown.

The Prime Minister. There is no post, I swear, which would not be worthily filled by the husband of Mrs. Macheath, But what are his particular attainments?

Polly. He has had great experience of the sea, sir.

The Prime Minister. The sea? Why, then, he shall have charge of the King's Coastguards, and put down the smugglers. For since rum was forbidden by Parliament, few other commodities are imported any more, and our Southern coast is little better than a wine-shop.

Polly. Macheath is acquainted with all the known stratagems of rascals, by land and sea.

The Prime Minister. He is appointed.

Air XVII.—*The Bells of Houndsditch.*

> When woman sues
> Who dare refuse?
> Fal, lal, lal, la.

Scene XII.

Macheath. Diana Trapes.

Trapes. Noble Captain, I hope you will be one of us at my house to-morrow, when my husband has invited some of our No Rum Company to a supper, and afterwards is to make a speech. But you had better come early, for we have not a drop of wine in the house, and I think no man will endure my husband's speaking for long on those terms.

Macheath. Liquor is very hard to come by in these days, but your husband is rich. I know a rogue who for forty guineas will provide you with a cask of anything. But he will not deliver unless he be paid before-hand : for no man cares to be hanged for nothing.

Trapes. Here is the money, Let it be rum. I should prefer wine, but the Quality will drink nothing now but what is against the law. [*Exit.*

Enter Filch.

Filch. The *Jenny Diver* lies off Greenwich, Captain, as full of spirits as a lord.

Macheath. Why, then, you must find a market for her. But look no more to me, honest Filch, for I have been made Captain of the Coastguards, and must give up the smuggling.

Filch. I knew how it would be. Politics has turned more men virtuous than any other cause besides. But, Captain, I hopes you do not intend to be a trouble to your old friends.

Macheath. Fifty guineas, Filch, and you may do what you will. Few Ministers charge so reasonably.

Filch. Here is the money, Captain, and I am very sensible of your kindness.

Macheath. Wait but an instant, and I will give you my bond in writing.

Filch. Why, Captain, between men of honour this is not necessary.

Macheath. You are right. But such good feeling is so uncommon that I am moved to do you a service. Lady Badger, that was Diana Trapes, desires two casks of rum to-morrow, and will pay you twenty guineas. Here is the money.

Filch. This is a poor price.

Macheath. It is all she will pay. But out of friendship I will try her again. When do you land the goods ?

Filch. At midnight —by *The Three Nuns* at Battersea.

Macheath. Then if I can squeeze another guinea or two out of her I will await you there. If not, be happy with what you have.

Air XVIII.—*Dorothy's a fine Lass.*

When to his lair
    The jackal draws his prey,
The tiger's there
    To snatch the prize away.
Thus statesmen lying,
Advantage spying,
    Their friends betray.

Scene XIII.—A BEACH AT BATTERSEA : NIGHT.

Macheath (masked).   Coastguard Officers.

Coastguard. I see a boat, sir, putting off from the sloop.

Macheath. Lie close, my men, till they have the casks ashore, for we should never interfere with a man's work. And use no fire-arms, for, though they are desperate villains, these men are benefactors to the public, and gunpowder is ruination to good liquor. But knock them down when their backs are turned and bid them stand in the King's name.

Filch and Pirates *enter from the river with casks. The Coastguards seize them. Macheath seizes casks.*

Macheath. In the King's name, stand !

Filch. Who are you, sir ? Your voice is familiar.

Macheath. A King's officer, who will send you to the cart for this affair, unless you are rich. Your goods are forfeit, but fifty guineas will save your necks.

Filch. This is the sum I paid your Captain to be

free of his attentions. If this goes on the importation of liquor will become unprofitable.

Macheath. Show me the Captain's bond.

Filch. I trusted to his honour.

Macheath. This is the first time I ever heard that said of the Captain. Your money or your life!

Filch. That I should live to have those words employed against me! Macheath shall hear of this. Well, here is the money. There shall be questions asked in Parliament over this affair.

Macheath. Pass, friends! You are free, Officers, away! [*Exeunt, with casks.*

Scene XIV.—MACHEATH'S HOUSE : CASKS BEHIND A SCREEN.

Macheath. Filch.

Filch. The dog took everything. And now I know not how I shall explain matters to Lady Di, for if we do not fulfil our engagements our credit with the great is at an end.

Macheath. This is indeed a misfortune. I will have the fool dismissed. Do you leave the affair to me and I will arrange matters. I have a friend in Chelsea who will supply the lady.

Filch. Thank you, Captain. I don't wonder you have turned honest when wickedness is so hardly used as I have been.

Macheath. You are right. Call on me to-morrow and you shall join the Coastguards, which is a respectable employment and more profitable than smuggling. [*Exit Filch.*

Enter Diana Trapes.

Trapes. Captain, that villain of yours has played

me false. Tell me where he is to be found or I lose half my friends to-night.

Macheath. I have spoken with him. He was taken by some busybody of a Coastguard and lost his cargo to the King. The man was in sore distress and durst not see you himself. As for your trouble, I have a friend in Chelsea who may oblige you. But his goods are very exquisite, and come more costly than the others. Fifty guineas will buy a cask.

Trapes. Here is the money, Captain. No price is too high when my husband is to make a speech. Bring it with you, Captain. You will be very welcome to-night.   [*Exit*

Enter Polly.

Macheath. One hundred and eighty guineas, and fifteen casks of spirits ! Thus are intellect and energy rewarded. Polly, my love, we are rich. I shall now be able to employ a few more secretaries.

Polly. Oh, Macheath !

Macheath. Let one of the small casks be placed in the carriage, my dear. I have promised Lady Badger a little present of rum.

Scene XV.—LORD BADGER'S HOUSE.

Lord Badger, Diana Trapes (Lady Badger), Macheath, with six Secretaries, Polly, Jenny Diver, Lords and Ladies. They drink.

Lord Badger. My Lords and Gentlemen, it is six months since the Act for the Abolition of Rum received His Majesty's assent, and already we are gathering in the harvest of that excellent measure. The behaviour of the common people no longer spoils our honest repose. Assassins, cut-throats, informers, highwaymen, lacking the stimulus of rum, have abandoned their former callings and devote themselves with industry to the service of the rich.

A Lady. I cannot endure this prosy fellow.

A Gentleman. Take a little of this excellent rum, and you will think him SOLOMON himself.

Lord Badger. Last year, my Lords, the killings and woundings in the City of Westminster numbered eighty-two ; this year they are no more than fifty. Wives and husbands live in amity together and license has gone out of our streets. It is true there are certain low fellows who in violation of the law secretly distil a villainous sort of spirit in their homes ; but these, as a general rule, are deservedly punished by the loss of their sight, or perish miserably of their own poison. There are others also who seek by stealth to smuggle spirits across the sea, and would for gold corrupt the homes of the people ; but I think we may trust to the vigilance and daring of our gallant Coastguards to see that these supplies are diverted into the homes of the great, who know how to use them with moderation. And for my part I shall support the law with resolution, so long as we lack nothing. My Lords, charge your glasses and drink with me to the intrepid Macheath, who has this day, I doubt not, preserved from drunkenness a number of the poor. Macheath ! The Captain of the Coastguards !

All. Long live Macheath !

Air XIX.—*Why do the Bishops ?*
What is so fine
As wine ?
Then, friends, the cup
Fill up.

Youth's a season
Mocks at reason,
Temperance then is treason ;
Ah !
Temperance then is treason ;
Ah !

End of Act III.

[CURTAIN]

II

THE *LAST* CASE OF 'NEEDLE' ROKE

[Just to show that we could do it too.]

I

' A PRETTY woman forgives a woman once, a man twice, herself never,' laughed the Comtesse de Vidomme, with a flash from her lustrous yellow orbs.

A burst of laughter greeted the epigram. My eye roamed again the brilliant scene, the gleaming napery, the forks and spoons. A fitting frame for that strange gathering of men and women, Statesmen, Ambassadors, Financiers, Embezzlers, the flower of the Chancelleries of Europe.

It was Christmas Day, the festival of Peace. But why was the Russian Ambassador at Madrid spending Christmas at the Midland seat of Sir Leslie Crane, sometime Foreign Minister of Great Britain ? What was the Yugo-Slavian Minister at Stockholm doing there ? Why was that pale-blue automobile now purring in the avenue, with the cock of France stamped upon the carburettor ? These things could mean but one thing. War. Red war.

It was a thought to stagger the mentality of the most hardened young diplomat.

'Why is Lord Rendle staying at Whiteleas?' murmured a rich voice.

The girl at my side was very beautiful. There was a mystery in her dark hair. The lobes of her ears were perfectly formed.

But was she not also the niece of the Croatian Legate at Vilna ? It behoved me to be careful.

I parried the question with a light remark anent the weather. For I knew very well the *raison d'être* of Lord Rendle's sojourn at Whiteleas. Ever since his powerful orange automobile had purred up to the front-door the previous day he had been closeted with our host in the private apartments of the latter. The former (a celebrated bore) had come hot-foot from the Cabinet to urge Sir Leslie's resumption of participation in the destinies of his country. With that keen mind added to their armoury, the British Government would be the better able to play their cards with the Chancelleries of Europe.

But it was well known that Sir Leslie was devoted to his hobbies and his Tudor home. A passionate moss-collector, could he be seduced therefrom to the hurly-burly of statesmanship again ? Now, as he listened to the ceaseless pleading of his interlocutor, I saw that his face was haggard from the strain of his position.

'We have to find a formula,' said Lord Rendle, pausing weightily between each word. 'Without a

formula Europe is doomed. Find that formula and
Europe is saved. Forgive me,' he boomed, ' but here
I cannot speak more plainly.'

Sir Leslie nodded and a shadow swept his brow again.

'Find that formula,' continued Lord Rendle deliberately, ' and Croatia will sunder her connexion with
the Little Entente. Lithuania will join France.
France will join Lithuania. Russia will abandon her
Trilenko claim. Spain will come to an understanding
with Finland. Finland will form a *rapprochement*
with Lisbon. There will be a *démarche* in Turkey.
America will send a Note to the Lapps. There will
be Peace.' He paused. ' You know the alternative,'
he went on gravely. ' War. Red War.'

In my ears I seemed to hear the thunder of the guns.
Sir Leslie closed his eyes.

'We must find that formula,' said Lord Rendle,
developing his theme. ' And you are the man to find
it. Find that formula and Croatia will sunder her
connexion with the Little Entente. Lithuania will
join France——'

Sir Leslie sighed—the sigh of a man in torture.

' But Croatia is the key,' said Lord Rendle.

Spurred by some spur, I turned to the beautiful
girl beside me.

She was not there !

II

Where was she—Lydia Vampa, daughter of Croatia,
niece to a Legate—the girl with the mystery in her
hair ; the lobes of whose ears were somehow never far
from my thoughts ?

When I saw her face emerging from under the table

my heart gave a great leap of thankfulness. My suspicions, after all, were both base and baseless. I chuckled to myself at the paradox.

' I dropped my napkin,' she said simply, but she flushed as she said it, and once again that twinge of doubt stabbed me to the core.

I suppose she sensed my unconscious ratiocinations.

' Ah, you English,' she said, resuming her seat, ' you are so cold.'

III

Feast-day or fast-day, the cogs which move the wheels which drive the machine of diplomacy rest not. The men finished their superb Armistice brandy and staggered off to join the ladies. But I noticed that Lord Rendle drew Sir Leslie aside into the great library. ' We have to find a formula,' the statesman was saying, and the ex-Foreign Minister nodded silently, without words.

The door closed behind them. . . .

IV

' Dead.'

The word sent a strange thrill through me, with its suggestion of finality and decay.

' Quite dead,' said Lord Rendle again.

The body lay flat on the floor of the great library— Sir Leslie Crane, the man who might have saved Europe !

' This is murder,' said Lord Rendle ; ' there has been foul play. I had not left him a minute. I went up to my apartment for some confidential papers in connexion with a matter which I am not at liberty to reveal—I refer to our Secret Treaty with Chili

G

—promising to return immediately. On rejoining him, Sir Leslie was dead; breath had fled from his limbs. He had taken part in the Great Division.

'Before I left the room,' he continued in a minute or two, 'a woman entered, alleging she had business with Sir Leslie of urgent import. He begged to be left alone with her. When I returned she was gone.'

'Could you identify the woman?' said the Spanish Ambassador, with a flash of his well-preserved tooth.

'I could,' said Lord Rendle.

My heart stood still.

'I will say nothing more now,' his lordship went on. 'There were many who stood to profit by this man's extinction. Had he been successful in his search for a formula, Croatia would have had to abandon her designs on Southern Algeria. Abyssinian ambitions would have crumpled. The Serbs would have yielded. Germany would have driven a wedge between Rumania and the Bulgs. The Czecho-Jugos would have re-orientated towards the West. America would have sent a Note to the Finns. The hegemony of Southern Asia——'

Silently we stole from the room, recognizing the respect due to the apartment of death.

But the word 'Croatia' rang in my ears.

V

I ran hot-foot to 'The Crown.'

It was a fortunate chance that my friend 'Needle' Roke was taking a well-earned rest in the neighbourhood. I had seen enough of this mystery to know that none but he would un-raffle it. What a man!

An eccentric by nature, I was not surprised to find

him crawling about the floor of his apartment, chewing betel-nuts. ' Keeps the mind supple,' he used to say.

Briefly I unfolded the facts as we panted up the avenue, Roke tearing off his waistcoat buttons as he ran, a nervous trick which showed his intellect to be working at its best.

' Is there a servant with red hair in the house ? ' he snapped at last.

' No.'

' I was afraid you'd say that,' he returned. ' Williams, this case baffles me '; and taking out a pair of scissors he severed a tuft of his hair, another characteristic mannerism of this extraordinary man.

' Here is the body,' I said, leading the way into the library.

But I stood back, gasping.

The body had gone !

VI

Roke was after it like a bloodhound, and, while I still stood dazed, was leading the way into the large apartment adjoining. A huge billiard-table stood in the centre.

' What is this apartment ? ' he clicked.

' This is the billiard-room.'

' Right ! ' he snapped. ' And what day is it ? '

' Christmas Day.'

' Ah ! ' he said with a gleam of triumph. ' Then there is your body ! '

I gasped. The body lay face downwards on the sofa, dead.

Roke ignored it. He was scrambling in the pockets

of the table, plucking feverishly at the last button of his waistcoat.

'Roke,' I said, 'frankly, I can see no daylight. Are we to believe that a dead body has deliberately removed itself from one room to the other ? Or did the murderer return and change its location himself ? And if so, why ? Either hypothesis seems at first sight untenable.'

'There is something far stranger than that in this case,' he replied ; and he held up two white billiard-balls. 'Williams ! ' he said, and there was a sort of horror in his eyes. 'There's been some damnable work afoot here—damnable ! '

'Speak, Roke. What is it ? '

'I don't know yet,' was the grave response. 'But these balls *are both spot !* '

VII

Lord Rendle was beckoning us into the hall.

'Mr. Roke,' he said, 'Inspector Smoot is here. But such is the besotted folly of the police that I am withholding from them the material facts of the case.'

'You have done well,' said my friend, nervously plucking off his last remaining waistcoat button.

'The woman whose intervention in the library was the prelude to this terrible drama is the niece of the Croatian Legate at Vilna. I need not tell you what that means. I was at the time in search of a formula. Had the dead man found that formula, within three hours there would have been a *coup d'état* in the Croatian capital. The Quai d'Orsay would have accepted the *fait accompli*. Spain would have ceded Morocco. Japan would have scrapped her new battleship. The Serbian Minister would have revoked his resignation. Lithuania would have attached herself to the Little——'

Something made my eyes stray into the billiard-room. I gasped.

'What is the matter with you ? ' said Roke sharply.

For response I levelled a shaking finger.

The body had disappeared !

VIII

Patiently Roke was piecing the thing together.

'The tracks of a full-grown man in snow remain for eight days if there is no thaw,' said the inscrutable man.

'But there is no snow,' I cried.

'Exactly.'

Try as I would, I could not guess at his meaning.

'One thing I have established,' he went on.

I leaned forward eagerly, ready to gasp.

'There is some person, man or woman, who has a powerful motive for concealing this murder. What do you make of this ? '

The object in his grasp was an exquisitely jewelled hairpin. About the trinket hung a faint aroma.

'*Cherchez la femme*,' said his lordship grimly ; and I hated him for the remorseless logic of his speech.

Roke sniffed significantly.

'*Talc*,' he sniffed. 'The favourite perfume of the Croatian *cocottes*.'

IX

Come what might, I would be her friend.

At midnight I entered her apartment. She

undulated towards me, robed in a clinging Oriental wrapper, which somehow enhanced the lobes of her ears.

' Ah, you English ! ' she murmured ; ' you are so cold.'

I pressed my lips to hers.

The gesture seemed to give her confidence. Tight-lipped, she poured out her tale. Hour after hour. And what a tale !

' I believe in your innocence implicitly,' I said at last.

' Then you will do this for me, is it not ? ' she said, in her quaint broken English. ' Take this packet —hide it—bury it—eat it ; or your little friend is *ruinée*.'

My heart sank.

It was a packet of exquisitely jewelled hairpins.

X

' *Will you state the nature of your business with Sir Leslie Crane that night ?* '

The challenge rang out sharp in the crowded hall. The Ambassadors and their wives had long ago dis-robed for the night, and, summoned by Roke to witness the *dénouement* of his quest, now thronged the stairs in *negligée*. The Albanian Minister had neglected to bring his hair.

' I cannot.'

The girl's eyes were brave, though her nose trembled. The hand that held Lord Rendle's night-light shook a little ; but the iron features of the diplomatists were unbending. They believed her guilty.

And I—with the knowledge of that damning packet

now buried under the Great Elm—what was I to believe ?

Who knows ?

Then came a dramatic turn.

A sign from Roke, and Inspector Smoot stepped forward.

' Lord Rendle,' he said, ' I arrest you on a charge of the wilful murder of Sir Leslie Crane.'

' The body will be found under the Great Elm,' said my friend.

The Inspector gasped, a picture of stupidity.

Roke laughed, enjoying his triumph. ' Only a freshly-turned worm, Inspector, but very often a useful clue.'

XI

' Jealousy, my dear boy—political jealousy,' said Roke, as he loaded his favourite briar. ' Sir Leslie would have been a dangerous rival in the Cabinet. Lord Rendle was playing a double game—inviting with one hand, dealing death with the other. Oh, it is despicable ! '

My friend had been unraffling the tangled skein for my benefit. But I was as baffled as ever.

What was the significance of the two ' spot ' billiard-balls and the jewelled hairpins ? Why had I met the girl with the perfect lobes on the backstairs carrying a tray of viands ? And why had the dead man whispered those strange words to her that fatal night : ' *Rescue me at half-past nine* ' ?

Clearly he had sensed his peril. Then why had he appealed to *her* ? Was she his mistress ? Had he been her paramour ? Was he insured ?

I beat my head against the wall.

XII

Tiptoe the girl led me through the green-baize door, the lobes of her ears a-quiver with mischief.

' But this is Sir Leslie's private apartment,' I cried.

' Hush ! '

A tall figure rose from the bureau. I could not believe my eyes.

It was Sir Leslie Crane !

XIII

' Yes, my dear boy,' said the ex-Minister, ' Lord Rendle is the First Bore in Europe, and after thirteen hours of him I decided that death was the only avenue of escape. As it was he pursued me even in death, necessitating those changes of position which puzzled you so much. So soon as Parliament reassembles, I may safely come to life without fear of further molestation ; and Lord Rendle will be set at liberty. Till then——'

' But the *hairpin ?* ' I gasped.

' A loan, my boy,' laughed the diplomat. ' I affect a briar-pipe. Meanwhile I have not been idle,' and the sometime Foreign Secretary took two documents from his bureau.

One was a Special Licence in the names of Lydia Vampa and Ernest Williams. The other was—The Formula.

Europe was saved !

III

THE BETTER MAN; OR, ORPHEUS UNDONE

[THE Inconceivable Film Company (of Screenville, Cal.), having presented the whole of ancient and modern history and all the Old Testament stories with a snap to them, have now turned to the early classical legends for material. The following is a synopsis of their latest Super-Sensation. Operatic and all other rights reserved.]

I

THE Golden Fleece at her mast-head,

THE *ARGO*

breasts the blue waters of the Mediterranean, nosing for home.

Among the Heroes on board are men from the best-known families in Iolcus (Thess.), Captain Jason, Castor and Pollux, the sons of Boreas, singer Orpheus, seer Mopsus, former legislator Theseus, ex-murderer Tydeus, Old Man Nestor and others.

Proud of the trophy which has crowned their world-quest with success, but weary of roaming, the Argonauts find the days hang heavy on their hands.

They pass the hours with Love,

THE WORLD-OLD TIME-KILLER.

There is no lack of feminine society on board. Medea, aside from her fits of temper, is generally liked, but the Captain's bride now sulks in her cabin. Since she cut up her kid-brother Absyrtus and threw the pieces overboard she has never been quite the same girl.

Meanwhile, their chaperon away, the dark-eyed vamps of Colchis keep the ship smiling.

GLAUCE
(*Florence Ham*)
and
PROCRIS
(*Sadie Barnett*),
two virgins of Thessaly, lead the smile-party.
Procris, a no-account blonde, loves

SINGER ORPHEUS
(*Bert Raddleday*)

But Orpheus loves Glauce.

Orpheus, artist to his finger-tips, sensitive, temperamental, lean-bodied, conducts the ship's glee-party.

The Heroes, all raised in the infantry, are sick of the sea ; they sing their favourite song :

> ' Wearily bounds the *Argo*
>   Over the boundless blue,
> A Fleece of Gold is her cargo,
>   Hearts of gold are her crew ;
> Weary of endless motion,
>   Daily at dawn we pray,
> " Poseidon, God of the Ocean,
>   Let it be calm to-day." '

Among the basses, but as near as possible to the altos, sits

HERCULES
(*Jake Weasel*)
a good clubman.

He hates the choir-practices ; but he loves Glauce.

Glauce is an alto.

Orpheus, sensitive to a fault, is not satisfied with the

choir's performance. His trained ear detects a mess in the bass.

'LOOKS LIKE YOU GOT NO EAR FOR MUSIC AT ALL, HERCULES.'

The bitter words strike a chord of anger in Hercules, who is ever impatient of blame from a weaker man.

'NO, NOR ANY OTHER GIRL-TRICKS. BUT, SAY, I CAUGHT THE CRETAN BULL; AND WITH MY OWN HANDS DIDN'T I SLAY THE MANY-HEADED HYDRA? WHAT D'YOU KNOW ABOUT THAT?'

Singer Orpheus, jealous of the strong man's nation-wide publicity, breaks off the glee-practice.

II

Seer Mopsus, shy, reserved, lies dreaming on the deck all day, seeing visions. He too loves Glauce; but he don't let on. He just dreams about her.

MOPSUS

(*Sid Honeydew*).

III

Hercules seeks comfort from Glauce. Broad, taciturn, man of deeds, exulting in his rude strength, he presents a striking contrast to Orpheus.

But, aside from Glauce, all the women love Orpheus.

Glauce don't know who it is she loves. Sometimes she is drawn to Orpheus, singer, artist, melody-man; sometimes to the man of action, the he-boy, Hercules. Both boss-men in their profession, the choice is difficult.

'SAY, GLAUK, GUESS I'M SORE WITH THAT STRUMMER.'

'WHY, HERC, WHAT'S EATIN' YOU ?   YOU GOTTER
TAKE MORE PAINS AT THE PRACTICES, THAT'S ALL.'

'HUH !   RECKON I ROOTED UP AN OAK ON MOUNT
CITHAERON AN' FLICKED IT INTO THE SEA WITH ONE
HAND.'

'HUH !   GUESS ORPHEUS CAN SHIFT A FOREST WHEN
HE FEELS THAT WAY.'

(It is said that the rocks and trees and beasts and
birds upon Olympus follow Orpheus when he sings.
This has always annoyed Hercules, who can only
move one tree at a time.)

A WOMAN'S CHALLENGE.

'See here,' said Glauce—'could you pick out the
sail-mast an' chuck it in the ditch ? '

'Guess I could try,' said Hercules ; and he did try.

'BELAY THERE ! '

Captain Jason's voice from the poop.

'GUESS I'LL NOT DAMAGE THE SHIP,' said Herc.

But a woman is not so easily deceived.

'HUH ! '

cooed Glauce.

'GUESS ORPHEUS COULD.'

IV

Singer Orpheus, pricked by the mysterious spur of
genius, comes on deck with his lute, singing the famous
song that shifts the rocks.   All the Argonauts and
she-vamps follow him, dancing like they were just
come out of an insane asylum.

Only Hercules, to whom one tune is of course the
same as another, sits sulkily to one side.

'WHAT'S BITIN' 'EM, ANYWAY ? '

> ' Rocks and rivers, follow, follow,
> Birds and fishes, follow, follow.'

The song swells to its climax. It upsets everything. The mast of the *Argo* unships itself and follows Orpheus around. Blocks, ropes and tackle roam about the deck. Huge trees scud past on the port hand. Strange lunatic birds descend on to the ship in a high state of emotion, and brightly-coloured fish are seen doing high-jumps out of the sea. There is lightning.

Jason, on the poop, is worried some, but, being all charmed-up like the rest of the bunch, he don't say much.

The song ceases. The crew, worn out with emotional excitement, put the mast back and tidy up the ship.

Jason. ' SAY, BUD, AIN'T YOU GOT NO QUIETER DITTIES ? THAT SOUL-STUFF DON'T SEEM SAFE IN A SAIL-BOAT.'

All the musician in Orpheus rose in his gorge.

' THINK I'M A CHEAP ARTIST IN A DOWN-TOWN TEA-HOUSE ? I DON'T SING TO ORDER—SEE ? SAY, BOSS, RIGHT HERE IS WHERE I QUIT.'

He throws aside his magic lute and registers pique.

Procris, frivolous, empty-headed, appeals for lighter music.

' DON'T YOU KNOW ANY OF THE NEW SONGS, ORPH ? CAN'T YOU SING :

> " I know a little place
> Way down in Thrace " ? '

Orpheus registers nausea.

Even Glauce supports the shallower girl.

' DON'T YOU KNOW NOTHING IN THE LYDIAN MODE ? '

Glauce ! The woman he loves. . . . He raises his eyes to heaven.

' GREAT ZEUS ! WHATCHEW WANT TO SHIP ME WITH THIS BUNCH OF LOW-BROWS ? '

V

While the women cluster around Orpheus as usual, Hercules, incensed by the vocalist's success with the mast, sits apart, brooding revenge.

Stealthily he picks up the fallen lute.

CONVINCED THAT THE MAGIC IS IN THE INSTRUMENT AND NOT IN THE SINGER, HE GUESSES THAT, IF HE THROWS THE FORMER OVERBOARD THE LATTER WILL BE SHOWN UP.

But first he will prove his theory.

' BOYS AND GIRLS, GATHER AROUND AND HEAR HERC SING ! NOW I GOT THE TRICK-HARP I GUESS I GOT THE GOODS.'

The Argonauts gather around. But first Hercules hands his mighty club to Orpheus.

' SEE HERE, STRUMMER, THERE'S NO TRICKS TO THIS TOY. LET'S SEE YOU KILL A WHALE.'

Orpheus declines the challenge. Glauce is repelled by his seeming cowardice.

' LET'S HEAR HERC'S MUSIC.'

Hercules, triumphant, opens his mouth and sings. It is a low-grade performance. The Argonauts drown the song in laughter. Orpheus stops his sensitive ears and runs below.

Glauce. ' SAY, HERC, IF ORPHEUS CAN'T KILL A WHALE BETTER 'N YOU CAN SING WE'LL HAVE NO FISH FOR SUPPER.'

The strong man, registering extreme discomfiture, prays to Zeus (the boss-god of Old Greece) :

'GREAT ZEUS, WORLD-WIDE PROVIDER OF MISFOR-TUNES AND MESS-UPS, CAN'T YOU HAND US OUT SOME KIND OF A SEA-SERPENT, HURRICANE, QUICKSANDS OR SOMETHING, SO 'S WE CAN SEE WHICH IS THE MALE MAN IN A TIGHT CORNER, AND WHICH OF US HAS THE RED CORPUSCLES, THIS DURNED VOCALIST OR ME ? AND, SAY, ZEUS, LET THIS GIRL GLAUCE BE THE PRIZE.'

' Done,' said Glauce.

VI

The prayer is soon answered.

Seer Mopsus, waking up the first time in three days, says he has seen in a vision that the *Argo* is heading straight for

THE ISLAND OF THE SIRENS.

(The Sirens are two Nymphs, or Super-Vamps, who inhabit a rocky island, where they lure the mariner to destruction by the beauty of their song. It has been decreed by Fate, however, that if ever a man should pass them by unmoved they must die.)

Hercules, the practical man, immediately grasps the danger.

' SAY, MOP, HAVE YOU REPORTED THIS TO THE OFFICER OF THE WATCH ? '

' No good,' says Mopsus. ' Guess it 's Fate.' And he lies down to sleep again.

' Why are you going to sleep ? ' asks Glauce curiously.

' RECKON I KNOW I'LL NEVER GET YOU, GLAUCE GIRL. BUT IF I GOTTER DIE I'D LIKE TO DIE DREAMIN' OF YOU.'

Glauce is struck by the beauty of the reply.   She registers emotion.

VII

Sure enough they come alongside Siren Island, and there sit the two super-vamps in white tulle, waving their wet, white arms on a rock.

AGLAOPHEME AND THELXIEPEIA

(*Maisie Gupp and Prudence Martini.*)

They sang seductively—Aglaopheme, soprano, and Thelxiepeia, contralto.   And the refrain of their song was

'BUT YES, WE HAVE NO BASSES.'

When the Argonauts heard the song they were all worked up and began clambering over the side.   Only three men remained unmoved—Hercules, who had no ear for music, Orpheus, who was down below, and Mopsus, who was asleep.

Glauce.   'NOW, HERC, YOUR PRAYER IS ANSWERED. SAVE THE SHIP.'

'WATCH ME, KID.'

Hercules put his back to the bulwark and fought like a tiger with the maddened men.   'But yes, we have no Basses,' crooned the Sirens, and the magnetic power of their song,

THE SWEETEST SONG IN THE WORLD,

was greater than his mortal might.   The crew swept him aside and dived overboard like men possessed. They were soon seen on the rock, having fun with the Kiss-merchants.

'FETCH ORPH.'

When Orpheus comes on deck Glauce hands him the magic lute.

'SING THAT CRAZY TREE-JAZZ OF YOURS, ORPH. THE LIVES OF YOUR FELLOW-TOWNSMEN DEPEND UPON IT.'

Orpheus took his lute and sang his wild sweet song:

> 'Trees and mountains, follow, follow,
> Rocks and rivers, follow, follow.'

No mortal ear could resist that strain. The Argonauts, after a brief struggle, tore themselves from the Sirens' embrace and swam back to the ship. Hercules tied them up with rope as they came on board.

Meanwhile the Sirens registered chagrin.

But as Orpheus continued to sing they listened amazed to this hundred per cent melody that had spoiled the man-market for them on their own pitch. It got them.

They swam off to the ship and climbed on board. The Argonauts tore at their bonds and Hercules had to tie up Senator Theseus again.

Meanwhile Aglaopheme makes a dead set at Orpheus. She sings him a little high-brow piece she hadn't put across in years. Womanlike, she kind of sensed what sort of a guy he was. He was different from the or'nary shell-back sea-fellers she met. She was just about through with the tar-brigade, anyway.

ARTIST CALLS TO ARTIST.

When Orpheus heard her sing, he thought of his home-town. It was the first time he'd heard any Good Music in years—not since they sailed after the Fleece. He could tell an artist when he saw one.

He was sick of the low-forehead hero-clique and love-women on board. This was something new. It got him. 'PRETTY BOY, COME ALONG. WE GOT NO TENORS,' sang Aglaopheme and moved towards the ship's side, beckoning.

Orpheus followed, spell-fettered. Glauce pulled at his arm, but he was a lost man.

Hercules looks on sourly. Though the music bores him he is strongly attracted by the Sirens *as* Sirens. But Orpheus, as usual, has gotten the glad looks.

Thelxiepeia, however, has cast a friendly eye on the man of muscle.

'DO YOU SING TOO, STRANGER?'

Hercules, a true sportsman, never knows when he is beat.

'DO I NOT?'

Hercules opens his mouth and sings.

The Sirens stand aghast. Never in all their experience had they heard such singing.

They stop up their ears, dive overboard and rapidly swim away, forgetting even Orpheus.

The spell is broken. The ship moves on.

Orpheus and Hercules face Glauce. Two voices ring out together:

'I SAVED THE SHIP. THE PRIZE IS MINE!'

The dark-eyed girl registers scorn at both of them. Both men have succumbed, she thinks, to the meretricious charms of the Sirens. This is doing an injustice to Orpheus, whose interest in the girl was purely professional. But there it is.

'GUESS IT'S FIFTY-FIFTY, AFTER ALL.'

The proud girl turns to Seer Mopsus, who is still snoring.

' Hey, Mop ! An' how's the visions now ? '

' Dreamin' of you, Girlie.'

' Is there a little shack for two in it somewhere ? '

' There sure is.'

' Then wake up, Boy ; your dream comes true.'
They embrace.

Four Eyes look love to Eyes which speak again.

VIII

Way back of the *Argo*, Siren Island falls astern.

The decrees of Fate are immutable, changeless.
A man has registered indifference to the Sirens. They
throw themselves into the sea and are turned into
exceedingly sharp rocks.

IV

NOT CRICKET; OR, THE STOLEN BAT

[In case the promised film of Oxford should have trouble
with the Censor, we modestly submit a scenario with a
Message to take its place.]

I

' Gosh, you Chaps, I'm Late for Lekker.'

Donning cap and gown, John Sterling threw down
his bat and strode off the cricket-field in his white
flannels to St. Aldate's. Captain of Oxford though
he was, John never allowed a game to interfere with
his work. Now, as he walked up the High Street,
followed by admiring students from the female colleges,
capped and gowned like himself, he put the century

('CENTURY'—100 RUNS)

which he had just scored out of his mind, and prepared it (his mind) for Stubbs's Charters. He was taking Law, Science and Modern Languages.

There was one who watched John leave the wicket with compressed lips and a scowl in his heart.

JASPER SNELL,

a bad influence, type and protagonist of all those elements in the University life against which John had set his face, was

PLAYING CARDS BEHIND THE SCREEN.

Seth Adams (Balliol) was his *vis-à-vis* and between dices they discussed their plans. 'That swot,' muttered Seth through his scented cigarette, 'is not going President of the Union.'

'BET YOUR LIFE, CHUM,'

replied Jasper concealing the Ace of Trumps in his pads.

Meanwhile John strode on through the Broad Street seeing everywhere about him the traces of his work.

When John Sterling joined the University a term or two before, it was in a bad way. Every department, Sport, Academic and Social, was riddled with effeminacy. Many of the dons used perfume ; the Warden of Balbus powdered his face. Small wonder, then, that the students were worsted in the boat-races with Cambridge.

Former senior monitor of Eton, John Sterling determined that a change must be made. His first night in Oxford, hearing the Magdalen clock chime out a quarter-of-ten above the heads of the sleeping students, he took off his cap and, standing on the old-fashioned bridge, registered a vow.

' GUESS THIS ACADEMY'S GOTTA BE CLEANED UP.'

John began by cleaning his own college, Caucus. One night, single-handed, he went round the rowing-men's rooms and took away their hot-water-bottles. Jasper Snell had never forgiven him for this; but some of the manlier oarsmen rallied to his side and helped him to ignite a great bonfire of their hot-water-bottles in the courtyard. The fame (and the smell) of this ' bonner' spread over Oxford. That week Caucus went head of the river. Jasper, piqued, refused to stroke the boat, and John took his thwart as well as his hot-water-bottle.

ONE GOOD THWART DESERVES ANOTHER.

From that day Caucus never looked back, and once again the clergy began to send their sons to the college. But from that day Jasper vowed implacable hostility to Pi-John, as his enemies, or He-John, as his supporters, called him, hampering him at every turn.

Thorough in his methods, John set himself to gain the confidence of the boys by all-round prowess at sports. One by one he gained his Blue at Cricket, Rowing and Golf, and became Captain of the Beagles. He was made President of the Dramatic Society and led the debates at the Gladstone Club. Thus, one by one, every section of the students came under his spell, and soon a manlier tone vibrated through the University. The Dramatic Society ceased to perform plays by foreign authors of uncertain character and came out flat-footed for TENNYSON. The Cricket XI. gave up sweets. The Bullingdon Club stopped cracking whips in the quadrangle and wore plain clothes. And now on every side of him he saw healthy skins, straight backs and clean limbs.

But one stronghold remained to be captured. The Union Society was still girlish and slack. The officers manicured their hands and drank hot *crème de menthe,* and many of the debaters made their speeches lying down. This term John meant to go President. With the University Cricket Match to be won and his Final Examinations imminent it was a busy term. But the thought of

IRIS

gave him strength.

Iris Bray, Undergraduate (St. Columba), studied at the same lectures under Professor Mellow. And now John found her on their favourite form quietly taking notes. Under her old-fashioned academic hat she looked a picture of English womanhood.

FOR HER SAKE HE HAD WON THE NEWDIGATE with a poem on HENGIST and HORSA.

But he was not clever, believing that character was more than cleverness; and Iris helped him at the Lectures, explaining the long words in her girlish whisper.

To-day was John's birthday and Iris had a present ready for him, which she handed to him with a graceful gesture during a lull in the lecture.

' I HAVE BROUGHT YOU A BAT.'

Their eyes met. With a woman's unerring instinct she had hit upon the very thing to give him courage and confidence in his exacting tasks. All the summer he had wanted a bat.

The old Professor noticed the charming incident and averted his gaze with a sigh. Sixty years earlier a girl had given him a bat.

A BAT.

Symbol of British manhood. Hewn out of Canadian pine. An Imperial bat. A bright new shiny unwounded bat. But Iris had an eye for decoration, and she had had it bound with strips of plaster, like the bats of great men which she had seen, to distinguish it from the ordinary naked bat. With her own fond hands she had tied to the handle a bright red ribbon, and on the birthday-card which hung from it she had written lovingly :

' MAY YOU HIT MANY WICKETS WITH THIS ! '

John vowed that the bat should go with him always, like the magic sword of KING ARTHUR :

' HIS " EXCALIBUR." '

II

And so the days drew on to the Presidential Election at the Union. John spoke at all the Debates, sometimes two or three times, and always the bat went with him. His versatility was the amazement of all, for he used to speak on both sides.

Only Iris knew the source of his inspiration, and indeed his statistics. Those late nights in the Bodleian Library, and a pale girl patiently reading up the Fiscal Question in the Debater's Encyclopædia. . . !

Where, the boys asked, did Oxford's captain and wicket-keeper find time to swot up politics to such effect ? Excluded from the floor of the chamber by the antiquated laws of the society, Iris sat above in the gallery, her large eyes inspiring the speaker like two electric torches. And after the Debates John would go out and run far off into the country with his long easy stride, still carrying his bat, for he was in training for the Beagles.   And Iris ran with him.

The effeminate clique at the Union, headed by Jasper and Seth, strained every nerve to stay his progress. They sat in a sullen group at the back of the hall, ate bulls'-eyes and interrupted.   Violating the rule against canvassing, they treated Freshmen to ices on condition that they voted for their own candidate, an æsthetic weakling called Phelps.   All in vain.   John's speeches for and against Tariff Reform blew Phelps out of the water, and the unmanly hisses of Jasper and his gang were drowned in a flood of cheers.

Cunning failing them, the opposition pondered force. The Thursday before the election is the Distinguished Strangers' Debate, at which the rival candidates cross verbal swords with each other and with great men from London.   On their performance at this ordeal the votes of thousands of undergraduates depend.

This term, attracted by the fame of John's doings, the Prime Minister had consented to take part in the debate.

The subject set for discussion had for many weeks been keeping Iris awake :

' THAT IN THE OPINION OF THIS HOUSE ART IS
BETTER THAN SCIENCE.'

John was to speak second, opposing the motion ; but by the Sunday, as usual, Iris had a speech prepared on both sides.

It was a full week for John.   By day the match against Worcestershire, by night rehearsing for the O.U.D.S. performance of *Maud*.   Between tea and dinner he sang with the Bach Choir ; before breakfast he wrote essays for his tutor. All this, with lectures and his fencing, took up much of his time. Small wonder that he was caught napping. For meanwhile

SETH AND JASPER MACHINATED ON.

Saturday night John read a paper to the Emerson Society at a nearby college. Jasper was there, and after the applause had died down offered John a glass of mulled claret.

'NO HEEL-TAPS, CHUM.'

A challenge no Oxford man who calls himself a man can refuse.   John looked at the innocent liquid, little knowing, in fact not knowing at all, that Jasper had secretly dropped into it some cigarette-ash. The most cowardly weapon in the armoury of an undergraduate. On Monday he had to make a century. On Thursday he had to argue with the Prime Minister. But the eyes of the Emerson Society were on him. One gulp and the glass was empty.

Too late he realized what he had done.

'YOU CUR!'

But his blow missed its mark, for already the deadly fumes had begun to do their work. Oxford—Worces-tershire—Iris—Emerson—rotated in his brain. He staggered out and raced for his College before the liquor should overwhelm him.

'Gated, I think,' leered Jasper.

'RUSTIGATED'

answered Seth, 'I fancy.'

The two laughed at the wicked jest.

And meanwhile the Captain of Cricket staggered through the City of Steeples. A proctor saw him and

gave chase.   He did not know that his quarry had won
the Four Mile hurdles against Michigan.   Intoxicated
as he was and hampered by his bat, John covered the
half-mile in thirty seconds level.   The proctor abandoned the pursuit and died a few days later.   But
as John neared the great gates midnight began to
strike. . . .

ONE . . .

TWO . . .

THREE . . .

(and so on up to twelve).

Too late !   The last stroke was silent as the panting
athlete raised his bat to batter on the forbidding portal.

A thought stayed his bat.   To rouse the sleeping
janitor at this hour would mean disgrace—ruin.
‘ Gated ’ certainly—perhaps rusticated—expelled.   His
scholarship taken away.   And the Union !

The match with Worcestershire could be postponed,
but not the Prime Minister—not the Election.

‘ THE GARDEN WALL ! ’

The wall of the College Garden was fifty feet high,
covered with barbed wire and surmounted by broken
bottles.   But to the athlete it was the work of a minute
to scale it.

Saved !

A movement in the deserted alley below attracted
his attention.   The moonlight shone upon an evil
face smiling sardonically up at him through the barbed
wire.

JASPER !

His enemy slouched away into the shadow.   But
what was that he carried ?

THE BAT!

John had dropped his bat.   Jasper had gone off with John's bat.

IRIS'S BAT. . . .

John cursed in the moonlight and fell into college.

III

The day of the Distinguished Strangers' Debate. . . .

Since that fatal Saturday night nothing had gone right with John Sterling.   He had saved his name and his scholarship, true ; but he had lost his bat. And the power seemed to have gone out of him.

The match with Worcestershire had been a fiasco, a massacre, a holocaust, a calamity.   Worcestershire won the toss and put Oxford in.   Then they put Oxford in again.   They put Oxford in again and again, and still Oxford made no runs.   Worcestershire won by three innings and 2,040 runs.   It was nearly a record.   The Oxford captain had disgraced himself. Without his bat he could not keep wicket, he could not bowl.   Worcestershire scored 351 byes.

He would not tell Iris what was the matter.   He had bought a new bat and disguised it as hers.   But, womanlike, she knew.

At the Bach Choir he was twice pulled up for singing flat.

And already the students were saying that a man who could not bowl better than that had no right to be President of the Union.

In his spare time he hunted for Jasper ; but Jasper had disappeared.   His scout said he was ' eating his dinners ' at the Bar.

John gnawed his cheeks.

The great hall of the Union was packed. The Officers came in. The Prime Minister came in. Sir Reginald Rickneck came in. Phelps came in. . . .

But where was John Sterling ?

Iris, gazing anxiously from the gallery, looked everywhere for him. She looked under the seats. She looked in the despatch-box. He was not there. . . .

' Funked it, chaps,' the callous boys were whispering at the back.

On his way to the Debate an unseen hand had thrust a note into John Sterling's hand :

' COME TO 657, BANBURY ROAD, AND YOU SHALL HAVE YOUR BAT.'

No. 657 ! North Oxford ! Five miles away. But there was still time. And it was worth it. With Iris's bat in his hand John knew that he could make the speech of his life. Without it . . . ?

A horse-tram lumbered by, full up. John Sterling vaulted on to the horse's back. And

MEANWHILE

the contemptible Phelps advances to the table and begins his speech. . . .

And Iris glides from the gallery into the street. She fears the worst. She is right.

Her brother's rooms in the Cornmarket. . . .

' LEND ME A PAIR OF TROUSERS.'

Paul Bray belongs to the Dramatic Society. He is famous for his skill in ' making-up.' With a few deft touches and a pair of white flannel trousers he transforms the girl into the living image of John Sterling. And meanwhile John Sterling lies gagged and bound